INTRODUCTION TO
BIOLOGY
LABORATORY MANUAL

BIO 110/BIO 110L

Damon Ely | Monty Vacura
Orange County Community College

Kendall Hunt
publishing company

TABLE OF CONTENTS

Introduction V

Laboratory Safety Procedures vii

Chapter 1.   The Scientific Method and Experimentation. 1

Chapter 2.   The Metric System, Measurement, and Graph Analysis 11

Chapter 3.   Atoms, Molecules, Acids, and Bases. 23

Chapter 4.   Factors That Affect Enzyme Activity. 37

Chapter 5.   The Compound Microscope. 53

Chapter 6.   Cell Structure and Function 59

Chapter 7.   Cell Transport: Simple Diffusion and Osmosis. 71

Chapter 8.   The Cardiovascular System 85

Chapter 9.   The Respiratory System 97

Chapter 10. The Digestive System 103

Chapter 11. The Urinary System. 115

Chapter 12. Nervous and Sensory Systems 125

Chapter 13. Dissection of the Frog. 145

Chapter 14. DNA Biology. 153

Chapter 15. Mitosis. 163

Chapter 16. Meiosis 175

Chapter 17. Reproduction and Early Embryonic Development. .183

Chapter 18. Patterns of Inheritance: Mendelian Genetics and Beyond 197

Laboratory Glossary. 213

INTRODUCTION

Ely and Vacura BIO 110 Lab Manual

The Introduction to Biology Laboratory Manual by Ely and Vacura was created for first-year biology students to help them gain fundamental laboratory skills. The laboratory exercises are intended to strengthen students' understanding of the material covered in a corresponding lecture course.

Each chapter guides students through a subject with clear explanations, helpful diagrams, and easy to follow instructions. Learning objectives are summarized at the beginning of each chapter to provide clear goals and to reinforce key concepts. Each chapter is divided into more specific sections that include activities, investigations, and review questions to focus students' understanding of discrete topics.

Student Learning Outcomes:

A) Students will demonstrate an understanding of how scientists use observation, hypothesis development, measurement and data collection, experimentation, evaluation of evidence, employment of mathematical analysis to explore natural phenomena and demonstrate application of scientific data, concepts, and models in the biological sciences.

B) Describe the basic structure of atoms and organic molecules. List the differences and similarities as well as the roles in cellular and organismal functioning between carbohydrates, lipids, nucleic acids, and proteins. Be able to state how the respective monomers and polymers are formed and the processes that break them apart.

C) Be able to state the characteristics of living things. List the major structural components of the cell and their functions. Be able to describe at an introductory level the basic cellular processes including energy transformations and cell transport.

D) Describe the basic anatomy and physiology of the systems of the body that include the: circulatory, integument, respiratory, digestive, excretory, endocrine, and nervous systems.

E) Be able to describe at an introductory level the basic cellular processes including DNA replication, protein synthesis, mitosis and meiosis.

F) Be able to describe the reproductive systems and the early stages of embryo development.

G) Describe the terms of genotype and phenotype and be able to apply knowledge obtained on how certain traits are inherited in basic Mendelian genetics.

LABORATORY SAFETY PROCEDURES

Please read the following contract. Your continuation in this course confirms that you have read the information within this document and agree to abide by these rules during your tenure in this laboratory course.

1. No eating, drinking or smoking in the lab. This is a state regulation as well as OCCC policy.

2. Microscopes are expensive instruments, to be handled with great care. You will receive instructions/guidelines from your laboratory instructor on proper use of these instruments. If you miss the laboratory where this information is provided, contact the laboratory instructor and obtain that information before using the microscopes in the lab.

3. When using chemicals and stains, follow your instructor's directions for safe use and disposal. Familiarize yourself with the locations of the sinks, eyewash station and fire extinguisher in case of an emergency. Wear gloves and protective eyewear as instructed.

4. Discard any dissection materials as directed by the instructor.

5. When using potentially hazardous material (chemicals, sharps like scalpel blades and microorganisms), dispose of those materials in appropriately marked containers.

6. <u>Wear Proper Attire</u>

   - Bare feet are not allowed in the lab; open-toed shoes/sandals are discouraged when working with dissection specimens and/or hazardous chemicals.

   - Spills may occur in the lab. Consider this before wearing expensive clothing.

   - Avoid excessively loose clothing and jewelry that can cause spills. Tie back long hair. Be mindful of others when handling chemicals.

7. Do not block walkways with bookbags/backpacks, etc. Know the fastest exit route out of the building in case of emergency.

8. Do not bring in dissection specimens (e.g., deer hearts) from home to dissect in lab class.

9. Leave the lab neat and your benchtop clean with your chair pushed in, hopefully the condition it was in when you entered the lab.

10. <u>If you are in doubt about any laboratory procedure, it is your responsibility to check with the instructor.</u>

CHAPTER 1
THE SCIENTIFIC METHOD AND EXPERIMENTATION

 Laboratory Objectives

By the end of this laboratory, the student should be able to:

- explain how scientists use the scientific method to gain knowledge;
- recognize the characteristics of a scientifically-valid experiment;
- provide definitions for the terms *scientific theory, hypothesis, falsifiability, replication, controlled variables, treatment, independent variable,* and *dependent variable.*

Science is a way of knowing. More specifically, *science is a structured investigative process* to achieve understanding of a subject. Scientists conduct their investigations in many ways, but the overarching concepts are consistent. All scientific investigations require curiosity, attentive observation, accurate recording of data, and articulate descriptions of methodology.

Many scientific investigations involve conducting an *experiment* to see how one variable affects another. A proper scientific investigation is performed with many considerations in mind, (e.g., are there extraneous influences that have not been controlled for? Are the results reproducible? Have all possible sources of error been considered?)

When an experiment is completed, and scientists feel confident in their conclusions, the next step is *publication* in a scientific journal. Scientific articles go through a rigorous process of *peer-review* where other scientists scrutinize the work to ensure it is of sufficient quality. Scientific journal articles represent our most current understanding and are read by scientists all over the world.

There are two general approaches to "doing" science. Often one approach leads to the other as scientists learn more and more about their subject. Both approaches aim to answer a *question*, the cornerstone of all scientific activity, but they differ in the steps taken to reach that answer.

- **Discovery-based science** (aka descriptive science) is the careful recording of observations in nature. This type of science answers the "what", "where", and "when" types of questions (e.g., "What was the atmospheric CO_2 concentration during the Jurassic period?"; "When is the breeding season of the gray tree frog?"; "Where are soil arsenic concentrations highest?")
- **Hypothesis-based science** is used to answer the "how" and "why" types of questions to achieve understanding of the reasons behind the observations produced by discovery-based science. These are the cause-and-effect relationships that allow us to predict future outcomes, (e.g., "Why are amphibian populations declining?", "How do DNA mutations arise?", or "How does climate change affect local plants and animals?")

The data produced by discovery-based science provides valuable essential knowledge about a subject that often serves as the basis for hypothesis-based science. Consider this example:

- Tonya is monitoring the health of local streams by collecting physical, chemical, and biological data. She notices that all the streams with the lowest pH also have the fewest fish (discovery-based science).
- Tonya hypothesizes an explanation for this observation: low pH has a negative effect on embryonic development. She conducts a test by separating fish embryos into chambers of differing pH and then monitoring their development (hypothesis-based science).

? *APPLY YOUR UNDERSTANDING*

For each of the following pieces of information, identify whether it the result of discovery-based science or hypothesis-based science.

Eating red meat may increase your chances of heart disease. _hypothesis_

The population size of smallmouth bass in Crystal lake is 2,280. _discovery_

2017 was one of the hottest years on record. _discovery_

Most physical traits are the result of natural selection. _hypothesis_

Chlorophyll is needed by plants because it absorbs light energy for photosynthesis. _hypothesis_

Hypothesis-based science is conducted with the scientific method as a guiding principle. The scientific method outlines the approach to investigating a research question in a formal, structured way (Fig. 1.2). Although it is not always strictly followed, the scientific method guides every scientific endeavor.

1. **Observation/Question**: Something must first be noticed to be investigated, and the observation is usually clearly stated within the research question. For example, in section 1.1 Tonya's question would be "Why are the fewest fish found in streams with the lowest pH?"

2. **Hypothesis**: *A hypothesis is a falsifiable explanation for an observation;* it is a well-reasoned answer to the research question. Tonya's answer to her question (i.e., her hypothesis) is that low pH interferes with embryonic development in fish.

   Falsifiable means that the hypothesis could possibly be disproved by the evidence. For example, a hypothesis that proposes a magical cause for the observation is not falsifiable—there is no test that could show that magic *wasn't* responsible.

3. **Test**: The experimenter tests the hypothesis by formulating one or more *predictions* that, if shown to be true, support the hypothesis.

> **"Educated ~~guess~~"**
>
> Most scientists do not define a hypothesis as an "educated guess" because the term *guess* implies a large degree of uncertainty, regardless of education.
>
> A good hypothesis is built upon the most current understanding of every aspect of the research and often requires careful review of the literature and many conversations with other scientists.
>
> Hypotheses are constructed with strong confidence, they are much more than mere guesses.

It is important to see the difference between a hypothesis and a prediction. A hypothesis is the explanation you use as a basis to make specific predictions about what will happen. Tonya might predict all the following: 1) fewer embryos will survive and develop at low pH, 2) adult fish will not be affected by low pH, and 3) embryos developing in higher pH will not survive even brief exposures to low pH conditions. If all these specific predictions are true, Tonya has strong support for her general hypothesis.

4. **Results/Conclusions**: Scientists analyze data using graphs and statistics to reach their conclusions. If the hypothesis is not supported (i.e., it is rejected) then another, *alternative* hypothesis is formulated and tested (Fig. 1.1).

Understand that *hypotheses cannot be proven*, they can only be disproven. The data

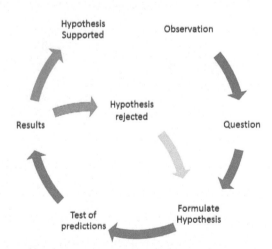

Figure 1.1 The scientific method.
Source: Damon Ely

collected may support the hypothesis, but another scientist may eventually produce an alternative hypothesis with greater support, changing our understanding. A negative result, though, is conclusive evidence that the proposed hypothesis is incorrect.

If the hypothesis is not supported, the researcher must either revise the hypothesis or construct an alternative hypothesis and carry out another experiment. Often, scientists will anticipate alternative hypotheses before starting their experiment and test all of them at the same time.

HYPOTHESIS VS. THEORY

When many related hypotheses have been validated, a scientific theory may emerge. A **theory** is a fundamental understanding of how some aspect of nature works, and it can weave together facts and evidence from several scientific fields. Both theories and hypotheses explain why certain events occur, and both make predictions that can be tested. However, hypotheses focus on explaining smaller, more specific events while theories are broader in scope and explain a wider variety of phenomena. For example, the theory of natural selection can be applied to hypotheses explaining why a peacock has such an exquisite tail, why some bacteria are resistant to certain antibiotics, and why some plants occur only in some parts of the world.

APPLY YOUR UNDERSTANDING

Read the following scenario and answer the questions that follow.

Jared is packing for a camping trip and he remembers that he will need a flashlight. He finds his flashlight and pushes the button to see if it works but no light appears. He thinks, the batteries must be dead and replaces the batteries with new ones and pushes the button, but no light appears. Now Jared thinks maybe the light bulb has blown and replaces the bulb and pushes the button; the light appears, and the flashlight is working normally. Jared looks at the old bulb and thinks it must have burned out.

1. Jared is using a process like the scientific method to solve his problem. State Jared's **question**: _why isn't the flashlight working_

2. What is Jared's first **hypothesis**? _Batteries are dead_

3. What *prediction* does he **test** for this first hypothesis? _putting batteries in that are new_

4. Write Jared's second hypothesis, followed by the prediction he tests. _The bulb is the actual problem_

5. What is his **conclusion**? _Not batteries — it was bulb_

(Remember: you cannot prove a hypothesis. Imagine that the light bulb in this example really was in working order. Perhaps a loose connection in the wiring of the flashlight prevented it from working (this is a hypothesis Jared did not consider) and in the process of replacing the batteries and bulb he somehow secured the connection, making the light appear when he finally replaced the bulb. This is an example of how we cannot deal in absolute truths in science—even when tests turn out as predicted, the possibility of an alternative explanation still exists.)

1.3 SCIENTIFIC EXPERIMENTATION

When scientists conduct an experiment, they consider many factors to ensure that errors are avoided and that the experiment adequately tests the hypothesis.

The experiment must be **controlled**.
Experiments often compare the results of two or more test groups that differ *only* by the factor of interest, all other conditions are kept the same. Typically, the control group either lacks the factor entirely or is the "normal" condition. This ensures that any differing results between groups is not due to some other factor not being investigated.

Control and treatment groups should be sufficiently **replicated.**
Multiple, identical *replicates* of the treatment groups should be conducted simultaneously. A conclusion should not be reached from a single outcome; at least three replicates are desirable. Consistent outcomes among the multiple replicates increases confidence in the results.

Replication also safeguards against unforeseen events that may cause the loss of an experimental group (e.g., a dropped test tube). Typically, the average response of the replicates within a group are calculated and compared to the other groups using statistics, which accounts for the variation among the replicates.

Randomization is important whenever subjects are being chosen to participate in a study.
For example, a study conducted to test the effects of a new medication may separate people into two groups—one that receives the medication and another that receives a placebo. By randomly choosing who is placed in one group or the other, there is no potential for any kind of unintentional biases towards age, gender, etc. . . that might affect the outcome. In a sense, randomization is a way of controlling the experiment.

Reducing human **error** is an integral part of every scientific experiment.
A good scientist always anticipates sources of error. When possible, a single observer should make all the necessary measurements to reduce any observer bias in the reading of instruments or use of a tool. Gloves and masks not only protect your health when worn, but they also prevent you from contaminating the experiment when handling chemicals or sensitive equipment.

<u>Studies of cause-and-effect relationships should clearly establish the **independent variable** and the **dependent variable**.</u>

An experiment often tests a cause-and-effect relationship between two variables. The *independent variable* is the "cause" that leads to an "effect" in the *dependent variable*. A scientist will typically change the independent variable (e.g., increase the temperature, lower the pH) and then measure the response of the dependent variable.

Exercise Follow the procedures below using the prepared materials in the laboratory. Read through all the procedures before you start and locate the materials you need. Wear the protective gloves provided by your instructor when handling solutions.

TEST FOR THE PRESENCE OF STARCH IN TWO UNKNOWN SOLUTIONS

Locate the following items:

- 2 solution bottles marked "Unknown X" and "Unknown Y"
- Starch suspension
- Iodine
- Distilled water
- 8–12 clean test tubes

You will design a simple test to determine which unknown, X or Y, contains starch. When you are ready to prepare your test tubes, add ten drops of the test substance followed by three drops of iodine and gently swirl the test tubes until mixed. Record any color changes, or no change, in Table 1.1.

You must create a *positive (+) control* to know what a positive result for starch looks like.

Write down how you will prepare a *(+) control*: _____

You must create a *negative (–) control* to know what a negative result for starch looks like.

Write down how you will prepare a *(–) control*: _____

What will you need to do to make sure the experiment is properly replicated? _____

How will you organize your results? Before you begin, create columns with labels in the top row of Table 1.1 according to your study design.

Table 1.1   Results of Starch Test

Final Color	

CONCLUSIONS

?

1. Which unknown solution, X or Y, tested positive for starch? _____

2. Describe some of the reasons why your experimental design gives you confidence in your final determination. _____

_____

_____

3. What could you have done to strengthen the test even more? _____

_____

_____

4. Describe any sources of error that may have occurred. _____

_____

_____

APPLY YOUR UNDERSTANDING

1. Identify which variable is the independent variable and which is the dependent variable for each of the following experiments.

    A. Sara wants to know how changing the temperature of the aquarium water would affect the breathing rate of her goldfish.

    Independent variable: _____   Dependent variable: _____

    B. Lucas wants to determine how tall corn would grow if different amounts of light were provided.

    Independent variable: _____   Dependent variable: _____

    C. Petra found a strong relationship between the abundance of deer ticks and the abundance of their host, the white-footed mouse.

    Independent variable: _____   Dependent variable: _____

2. **Case Study—Louis Pasteur Refutes Spontaneous Generation**

If food or drink is left out, you know that it will "spoil"—microorganisms like bacteria and fungi will soon appear. People once thought these microorganisms arose spontaneously from the food, that the food suddenly "became" the microbes that made it inedible. This idea was called Spontaneous Generation. However, a French microbiologist named Louis Pasteur disagreed, and he had an alternative hypothesis.

In 1859, Louis Pasteur provided experimental evidence that bacteria contaminated the food by riding dust particles in the air. Pasteur did not agree with the idea that life could arise spontaneously—his notion was that life must originate from life itself. In that year, the French Academy of Sciences sponsored a contest and offered a prize for the best experiment to address Spontaneous Generation. Pasteur won the contest with a simple but elegant experiment.

Pasteur set up his experiment by preparing nutrient broth within numerous glass flasks that had curved necks shaped like a sideways letter S. The flasks were still open to the air, but dust particles could not make their way to the broth because of the S-shaped neck. He boiled the broth to sterilize it and then left it untouched. The broth remained sterile day after day in all the flasks.

Pasteur then broke off the necks to expose the broth directly to the air. A population of bacteria appeared within one day in all the flasks. Pasteur's findings helped us understand that diseases could be prevented if steps were taken to avoid the contamination of food and wounds.

A. What was the initial observation that led to Pasteur's experiment? Remember, the observation is <u>what is first noticed or recognized</u> and leads them to perform the experiment.

_____

_____

B. What was Pasteur's hypothesis? Do this: State the observation (your answer to part A), write the word "because", and then complete the sentence with Pasteur's explanation.

_____

_____

C. What prediction(s) did Pasteur make to test his hypothesis? Predictions typically take the form of if-then statements.

_____

_____

D. The reviewers unanimously agreed to award the prize to Pasteur because the results were so convincing. What specific feature of the design of the study helped to increase the strength of his findings?

_____

_____

E. Pasteur's experiment provides support for a more general theory that rejects the notion that living cells can spontaneously arise from nonliving materials. What is the more general theory being supported?

_____

_____

3. **Case Study: Can Moxibustion Reduce the Incidence of Breech Birth?**

From: Cardini, F. and H. Weixin. 1998. Moxibustion for Correction of Breech Presentation. *Journal of the American Medical Association*. Volume 280 (18): 1580–1584.

A scientific article in the *Journal of the American Medical Association* concluded that the risk of breech births could be lowered by an acupunctural treatment known as moxibustion. A breech birth occurs when the position of the fetus is improperly rump-first instead of head-first.

The moxibustion treatment involved heating a point on the smallest toe. The study randomly separated two hundred and sixty (260) women with at-risk fetuses into two groups of 130: those that received the treatment and those that did not receive any treatment.

Significantly more of the untreated women had breech births by the end of the study. The study reported that it was the first to conduct a randomized controlled trial to investigate this issue, but in the conclusions section of the article the authors state ". . . we think that the mechanism of action of moxibustion is not entirely clear and warrants further research."

This finding suggests that moxibustion is an effective treatment for breech births. Think like a scientist: Is this conclusion confirmed by the evidence in the report? Consider the following to help guide your decision:

A. Was this study properly controlled? Think about the *experiences* of the women in the two groups—were there any differences, unrelated to the effect of moxibustion itself, between the two groups that could have affected the results?

Explain _____

_____

_____

B. We expect a certain amount of natural variation in how different people may respond to any treatment. There are two important ways this study took natural variation into consideration as part of the experimental design. Describe these two ways. (Hint: Look back at Section 1.3—Scientific Experimentation)

_____

_____

_____

C. Are the results consistent with established science? In other words, can we explain the outcome of the experiment using our biological understanding? *Should* that be a consideration?

_____

_____

_____

CHAPTER 2
THE METRIC SYSTEM, MEASUREMENT, AND GRAPH ANALYSIS

 Laboratory Objectives

By the end of this laboratory, the student should be able to:

- measure length, mass, and volume using the metric system;
- measure temperature in degrees Celsius;
- successfully convert quantities among metric units of measurement;
- understand the difference between accuracy and precision;
- distinguish among bar graphs, line graphs, and scatterplots and know which type of graph is best for a certain set of data;
- correctly construct a bar graph, line graph, and scatterplot.

The metric system is the International System of Units (SI) used by scientists worldwide. Nearly all researchers report their findings with SI units because the metric system is based on 10-fold differences among units that, unlike the U.S. system, apply similarly whether measuring mass, volume, or distance. Although we in the U.S. still mostly weigh ourselves in pounds, plan our travel distance in miles, and measure liquids in ounces, cups, and gallons we sometimes encounter SI units, for instance, when we take a 200-milligram ibuprofen tablet or purchase a 2-liter bottle of soda.

Once measurements have been made, scientists often present their results using graphs. At a glance, graphs can quickly display differences and trends in the data. While graphs are easily made using computer programs, learning how to make a graph by hand is an important skill that will improve your insight when analyzing and interpreting graphs presented in textbooks and scientific articles.

This laboratory will give you experience using the metric system to make measurements, it will introduce you to some of the measuring equipment scientists use, and you will learn how to construct the common types of graphs scientists use to present their data.

We will use the metric system to measure length, mass, volume, and temperature. We begin learning about the metric system by learning the **base units** for each of these measurements (Table 2.1).

Table 2.1   The base units of metric measurement

Quantity	Metric (SI) Unit	Symbol
Length	Meter	m
Mass*	Gram	g
Volume	Liter	L
Temperature	Degree Celsius	°C

*The kilogram is technically the base unit of mass; we will use the gram to be consistent with the other units as we learn.

In the same way that we would convert 12 inches to 1 foot, we can convert amounts of the base units for length, mass, and volume using certain prefixes that have standard relationships to the base unit (Table 2.2). Table 2.3 shows the U.S. customary unit equivalents to the SI units for comparison.

Table 2.2   Prefixes for SI units

Prefix	Symbol	Value (in base units)
Mega-	M	× 1,000,000
Kilo-	k	× 1000
Hecto-	h	× 100
Deka-	da	× 10
Deci-	d	1/10
Centi-	c	1/100
Milli-	m	1/1000
Micro-	μ	1/1,000,000

Are prefixes used for temperature?

No, temperature is reported in degrees Celsius (°C) with no use of the prefixes in Table 2.2. For example, the surface temperature of the sun is 5,505 °C—you would <u>not</u> convert this value to 5.505 k°C.

The typical conversions made are between the Fahrenheit and Celsius temperature scales:

°F to °C: $°C = (°F - 32) / 1.8$
°C to °F: $°F = (°C × 1.8) + 32$

Table 2.3   Relationship of SI units to the U.S. customary units

Mass	Length	Volume
1 g = 0.0022 pound	1 m = 3.281 feet	1 L = 1.057 quarts

HOW TO MAKE METRIC CONVERSIONS

Metric conversions are made using the relationships to the base units (m, g, or L) shown in Tables 2.2 and 2.3. We will use **conversion factors** to convert a quantity from one SI unit to another. A conversion factor is a fraction that states the same quantity in different units in the numerator and denominator. For example, since 1 g = 0.0022 pound we can write a conversion factor in two ways:

$$\frac{1\ g}{0.0022\ pound} \quad and \quad \frac{0.022\ pound}{1g}$$

If we wanted to convert an amount in pounds to grams, we would use the first of these factors. As an example, the mass in grams of an object that weighs 0.500 pounds is found by

$$Number\ of\ grams = (0.500\ \cancel{pounds}) \times \frac{1\ g}{0.0022\ \cancel{pound}} = 2.27g$$

Since pounds is in the denominator of the conversion factor it cancels pounds in our given quantity of 0.500 pounds; only grams—the desired unit—is left in the numerator of our final answer. Conversion factors are arranged in such a way that the desired units appear in the numerator and the given unit appears in the denominator so that

$$\cancel{Given\ unit} \times \frac{desired\ unit}{\cancel{given\ unit}} = desired\ unit$$

PRACTICE CONVERSIONS—PART I

If a car has a length of 189 inches, what is the length in meters?

Solution: We know that 12 inches = 1 foot and, from Table 2.3, 1 m = 3.281 feet. We will set up our conversion factors so that inches and feet cancel, leaving only meters in the numerator:

$$Length\ in\ meters = 189\ \cancel{inches} \times \frac{1\ \cancel{foot}}{12\ \cancel{inches}} \times \frac{1\ meter}{3.281\ \cancel{feet}} = 4.80\ m$$

How many liters equal 1 gallon? (Note: there are 4 quarts in 1 gallon)
Show your work:

The previous examples made conversions between SI units and U.S. customary units. In the same way, we can use conversion factors to make conversions *within* the metric system. For example, suppose we wanted to express 10,200 liters in kiloliters (*i.e.,* L to kL). We see in Table 2.2 that the kilo- prefix represents 1000 times the base unit, thus

$$\text{Volume in kiloliters} = 10{,}200 \; \cancel{\text{liters}} \times \frac{1 \text{ kiloliter}}{1000 \; \cancel{\text{liters}}} = 10.2 \text{ kL}$$

We use the same methods as before when having to span multiple SI units. For instance, to convert 0.0326 kilograms to milligrams, the conversion would be

$$\text{Mass in milligrams} = 0.0326 \, \cancel{\text{kilograms}} \times \frac{1000 \; \cancel{\text{grams}}}{1 \, \cancel{\text{kilogram}}} \times \frac{1000 \text{ milligrams}}{1 \, \cancel{\text{gram}}} = 32{,}600 \text{ mg}$$

PRACTICE CONVERSIONS—PART II

Make the following conversions:

Length	Mass	Volume
3.2 m = _____ cm	1.2 kg = _____ g	4000 mL = _____ L
175 hm = _____ km	55 dg = _____ dag	0.732 kL = _____ cL
1350 mm= _____ m	29.3 g = _____ cg	68.4 hL = _____ dL

Which one is bigger? (circle the bigger quantity)

0.1 m or 10 mm   3.2 L or 320 mL   0.523 kg or 52.3 hg   3.0 m or 3000 cm

Make the following temperature conversions:

1. Water freezes at 0 °C, but its greatest density is at 4 °C. What is 4 °C in °F? _____

2. Room temperature is 72 °F. What is room temperature in °C? _____

3. Normal human internal body temperature is 98.6 °F, which is _____ °C.

4. The boiling point of water is 100 °C. Convert this value to °F. _____

Scientists use a variety of instruments and lab equipment to make measurements. A **beaker** (Fig. 2.1a) is used to prepare solutions and usually has a small, pointed spout to aid in pouring. A **graduated cylinder** (Fig. 2.1b) is taller and slimmer than a beaker and is used to make more accurate liquid volume measurements. Both the beaker and the graduated cylinder have "graduations", or measurement marks, indicating volume.

The **meter stick** (Fig. 2.1c) and the **hand ruler** (Fig. 2.1d) are common instruments used to measure length. Often, these items also have U.S. customary units printed on them, so it is important to be attentive to which scale you are reading.

The **triple-beam balance** (Fig. 2.1e) is used to measure mass. However, most laboratories are equipped with **digital scales** (Fig. 2.1f), some of which can measure very small masses with a high degree of accuracy.

A **thermometer** (Fig. 2.1g) is used to measure temperature. Most thermometers display both Celsius and Fahrenheit scales of temperature—read carefully.

Figure 2.1 Commonly-used laboratory instruments for measurement. a) beaker; b) graduated cylinder; c) meter stick; d) hand ruler; e) triple-beam balance; f) digital scale; and g) thermometer.

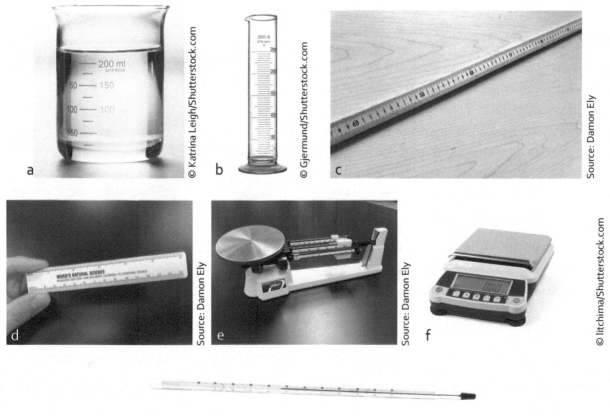

ACCURACY VS. PRECISION

Potential sources of error are a concern whenever measurements are made. If the observer is careful and the instrument is used correctly, the percent error is small, and deviations will lie on both sides of the true value. Yet variation will also occur naturally, especially in biological investigations (e.g., measurements of human birth weights). As discussed in chapter 1, multiple measurements are made (i.e., replication) to capture, and account for, any error and natural variation.

Two characteristics of measurements, their accuracy and precision, are scrutinized by scientists. **Accuracy** refers to how closely the measurements agree with the 'true' value, which may never be known. **Precision** refers to how closely the measurements agree with each other. For example, imagine you are using a digital scale, like the one in Fig. 2.1f, to weigh 1 mL of water but the scale is calibrated incorrectly—it is 0.20 g underweight. The known density of water is 1 g/mL so the true weight is 1.00 g; however, because of the incorrect calibration, you consistently obtain readings of a mass of 0.80 g. In this example your repeated measurements (and the scale itself) are highly precise, but not accurate.

MAKING MEASUREMENTS

Exercise 1

Practice making the following measurements using the different instruments available in the laboratory. Be sure to measure carefully and to report the correct SI units.

Measure Volume

Obtain two graduated cylinders and a beaker. Fill the beaker with water and use it to carefully measure 15 mL of water in one of the graduated cylinders. To ensure accuracy, you must keep the graduated cylinder flat on the countertop and read the meniscus line at eye level. The meniscus line is the lowest point of the curved surface of the water (see Fig. 2.2).

Then, measure 10 mL of water in the other graduated cylinder and pour this volume into the first graduated cylinder. If you have measured accurately, the final volume should equal 25 mL.

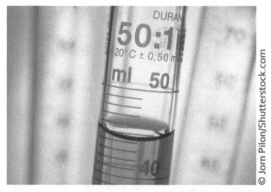

Figure 2.2   The meniscus line.

Measure Length

Use the appropriate instrument, either a hand ruler or a meter stick, to measure the following:

1. Index card: length _____cm, width _____cm; *convert to mm*: length _____mm, width _____mm
2. Tabletop length _____cm; *convert to m*: _____m
3. Your height: _____cm; *convert to m*: _____m

Measure Mass

1. Use the triple-beam balance to weigh either your mobile phone or the object that is available next to the balance.

    Object weighed: _____   Mass of object: _____ g

    Convert this mass to kilograms: _____ kg

2. Use the digital scale to weigh your pen and two of the small objects available next to the scale.

    Mass of pen: _____ g

    Object 1: _____   Mass of object: _____ g

    Object 2: _____   Mass of object: _____ g

Measure Temperature

Place a thermometer into the beaker with distilled water that has been left at room temperature and record the temperature in Celsius. Then, hold the thermometer in the warm water bath (make sure not to touch the bottom of the bath with the thermometer) and record the temperature in Celsius. Convert both temperatures to degrees Fahrenheit.

Water at room temperature = _____°C; convert to °F: _____°F

Warm water bath temperature = _____°C; convert to °F: _____°F

2.3 MAKING AND USING GRAPHS

Three types of graphs are commonly used by scientists: bar graphs, line graphs, and scatterplots. You will learn the differences in their appearance and use, but all graphs have the following features (see Fig. 2.3):

- **Caption**—a caption describes what the graph is showing like a title would; however, captions for graphs (aka *figures* in scientific articles) often provide more information than a title, such as the sample size, statistical results, and essential details about methodology and sample collection.
- **Labeled axes**—the horizontal or x axis displays the independent variable, which is the causal variable changed or set by the experimenter (in line graphs the x-axis is *time*). The vertical or y axis displays the dependent variable, which is the measured response to the independent variable. These variables must be labeled on the axis with both a simple word or phrase followed by the units of measurement.

- **Scales**—the axes have tick marks with evenly-spaced numbers that designate the scale of measurement. The experimenter must choose the correct scale to encompass all the data points and utilize the maximum amount of the graph's area.
- **Key/Legend**—when necessary, a key (aka legend) is used to differentiate among multiple datasets.

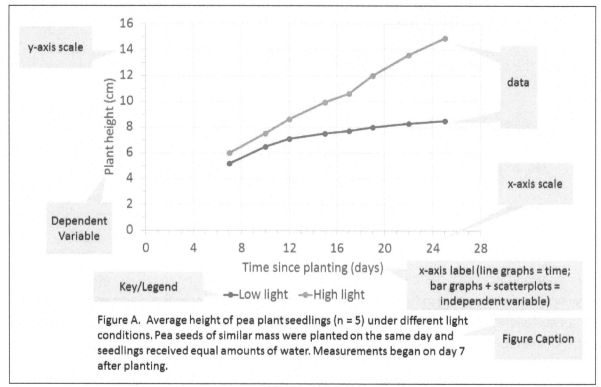

Figure A. Average height of pea plant seedlings (n = 5) under different light conditions. Pea seeds of similar mass were planted on the same day and seedlings received equal amounts of water. Measurements began on day 7 after planting.

Figure 2.3   Features of a graph.
Source: Damon Ely

COMMON TYPES OF GRAPHS

A **bar graph**, also known as a column graph or histogram, is used to compare categorical, or *qualitative*, data. The x axis of bar graphs does not have a quantitative scale; instead, categories or groups are displayed (e.g., female + male; Fig. 2.4a). The y-axis of bar graphs should begin at zero.

A **line graph** follows the progress of results over time. Data points are connected by a line to display periods of increases, decreases, or no change in the response variable (Fig. 2.4b).

A **scatterplot** is used to show a cause-and-effect relationship between two variables. Data points are not connected by a line in a scatterplot; instead, a computer program is typically used to create a trendline (a linear regression) that best represents the relationship (Fig. 2.4c).

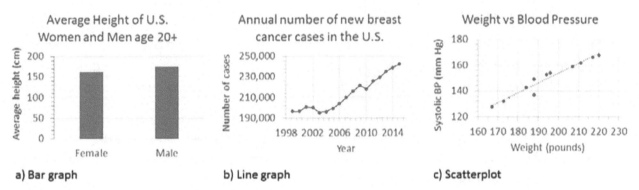

Figure 2.4   Types of graphs. *Data from U.S. Census Bureau (https://www.census.gov//)*
Source: Damon Ely

MAKING GRAPHS

Exercise 2

Practice making the different types of graphs by using the provided datasets. Be sure to correctly label the axes in neat handwriting, and to draw lines with the use of a hand ruler or a straight edge.

CREATE A BAR GRAPH

Carbon dioxide (CO_2) is a greenhouse gas that accumulates in the atmosphere and prevents heat from escaping, causing the earth's temperature to rise and disrupting global climate patterns. Most organisms produce CO_2 via cellular respiration, but the greatest cause of rising CO_2 concentrations (measured in parts per million, ppm) is the burning of fossil fuels by automobiles and coal-fired power plants. CO_2 concentrations have been monitored continuously since 1958 at the Mauna Loa Observatory in Hawaii, but scientists are able to measure more ancient concentrations by analyzing air bubbles trapped in ice cores taken from the Antarctic.

- Make a bar graph comparing CO_2 concentrations in the years 1000 and 2018.
- Label the y axis and choose a scale that uses most of the graph area.
- Create bars of the same width (use a ruler) centered over the tick marks on the x axis. Label the year under each bar.

Year	CO_2 concentration (ppm)
1000	280
2018	405

The bar graph you created shows a striking difference between past and present CO_2 concentrations, but it does not provide information about whether the observed increase was gradual or if it occurred suddenly. That analysis requires data from the many intervening years plotted on a line graph.

- Make a line graph showing CO_2 concentrations from the year 1000 to 2018.
- Label both axes correctly and choose scales for both that encompass all the data and maximize the use of the graph area.
- Plot each data point and connect them with a straight line (use a ruler).

Year	CO_2 concentration (ppm)
1000	280
1100	283
1200	284
1300	283
1400	280
1500	282
1600	276
1700	277
1800	283
1900	296
2000	372
2018	405

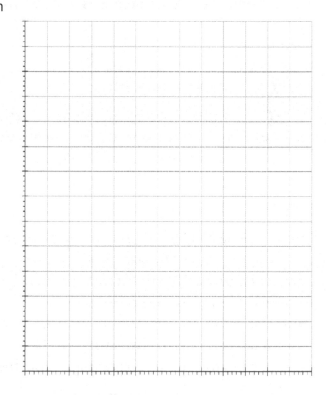

INTERPRET THE DATA

?

1. Between years 1000 and 2018, do CO_2 concentrations appear to rise gradually or are there sudden increases?

2. During which time period do CO_2 concentrations rise the most?

3. Critics of climate-change deny that it is caused by human activity. Search *Industrial Revolution* online to find the time period in which we transitioned from hand-powered to machine manufacturing. Do you think the CO_2 data strengthen the position that climate change has been accelerated by human activity? Explain.

The effects of climate change are widespread, and this continues to be a focused area of research by scientists. One of the primary concerns with rising temperatures is the melting of ancient glaciers because of the impact melting is expected to have on rising sea levels and biota worldwide.

Carbon dioxide emissions have risen steadily since the Industrial Revolution, resulting in higher atmospheric CO_2 concentrations and an increase in global temperature of approximately 0.9°C (1.6°F) during the past 200 years. Is there a link between CO_2 emissions and the amount of arctic sea ice?

CO_2 emissions (millions of metric tons)	Arctic Sea Ice Extent (millions of square kilometers)
7500	6.2
7800	6.1
8000	5.6
8400	6.0
8500	4.3
8700	4.7
8700	5.4
9100	4.9
9500	4.6

- Make a scatterplot of CO_2 emissions vs. sea ice extent.
- Be sure to correctly identify the independent and dependent variables by labeling them on the appropriate axes.
- Once again, choose your scale for each axis to encompass all the data and make full use of the graph area.
- Plot the x-y pairs of data as points on the graph but do not connect them with a line.

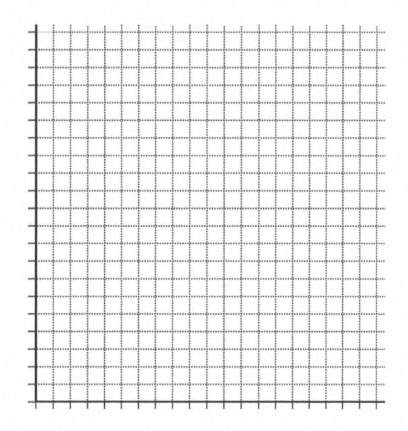

INTERPRET THE DATA

?

1. Does there appear to be a positive or a negative relationship between CO_2 emissions and arctic sea ice extent? Describe the observed relationship in a single sentence.

_____

_____

2. Why would it be unrealistic to expect the data points representing *global CO_2 emissions* and the *amount of sea ice in the arctic* to fall perfectly on a straight line?

_____

_____

3. The data for sea ice when CO_2 emissions were 8500 million metric tons appears to be an **outlier**—meaning that this data point is more different than we would expect considering all the other data. Outliers that are considered anomalous can be removed from the data under certain conditions.

   If the world returns to a CO_2 emission level of 8500 million metric tons at some point in the future, what amount of sea ice might we expect to achieve? Ignore the outlier, look at the trend, and provide an estimate.

_____

_____

CHAPTER 3
ATOMS, MOLECULES, ACIDS, AND BASES

 Laboratory Objectives

By the end of this laboratory, the student should be able to:

- determine the number of protons, neutrons, and valence electrons for elements 1–20 on the periodic table;
- understand the concept of stability and the octet rule;
- explain the difference between ionic and covalent bonds;
- draw the structural formula for a molecule when given its molecular formula;
- balance the reactants and products in a chemical reaction;
- understand the pH scale and the difference between acids and bases;
- use pH test strips, pH meters, and chemical indicators to measure pH.

All matter is composed of **atoms**—the small interacting units that bond together to form larger molecules. Learning about atoms and molecules is important to learning biology because they are the materials used by organisms to grow, maintain, and perform necessary reactions for homeostasis. Most of the molecules in your body are water (H_2O), and the remaining molecules are mostly composed of just six elements: carbon, hydrogen, nitrogen, oxygen, phosphorus, and sulfur.

In addition to learning atomic structure and the chemical bonds that form molecules, other chemical concepts of importance to biology are acidity, basicity (or alkalinity) and the pH scale. Along with temperature, pH is an important environmental condition to which life responds and adapts when changes occur.

This laboratory will help you understand the fundamental structure of atoms and why they behave (i.e., react) in certain ways. You will also learn the basis for understanding acids and bases and gain experience using the pH scale.

The **periodic table of the elements** (Fig. 3.1) organizes all the known elements into groups that have similar properties. At minimum, the table should provide the **element name, element symbol, atomic number,** and **atomic mass** for each entry.

The atomic number represents the number of positively-charged **protons** found at the center, or **nucleus** of the atom; the atomic number defines the element. Also residing in the nucleus are the **neutrons,** particles that do not have any charge (i.e., they are neutral). Surrounding the nucleus (in discrete levels of energy known as *shells*) are the negatively-charged **electrons**. Protons and neutrons are similar in mass (both have an *atomic mass unit* of 1), and both are much more massive than electrons. Although protons and electrons differ in mass, their charge is equal but opposite. Protons carry a +1 charge while electrons carry a –1 charge.

ELECTRON SHELL DIAGRAMS

To visualize an element, we can draw an electron shell diagram in its neutral form. A **neutral** atom is one where the number of electrons (negative charges) is equal to the number of protons (positive charges) resulting in an overall charge of zero. The following information will help as you continue:

- *Atomic number* = # of protons
- *# of neutrons* = Atomic mass (rounded) – atomic number
- *Neutral*: # of electrons = # of protons
- *Valence electrons*: electrons in the outermost shell only

We will construct an electron shell diagram for carbon, atomic number 6. Start by drawing a circle to represent the nucleus containing the correct number of protons and neutrons. Using the periodic table (Fig. 3.1), we see that carbon has an atomic mass of 12.011 which rounds down to 12. Thus, the number of neutrons = 12 – 6 = 6. So, carbon has 6 protons (p) and 6 neutrons (n):

The electrons surrounding the nucleus are organized into one or more shells. ***The first, innermost shell can only hold up to 2 electrons, while the others can hold up to 8***. Neutral carbon has a total of 6 electrons that balance out the 6 protons in the nucleus. We can only place 2 electrons in the first shell, leaving four to be placed in the second shell:

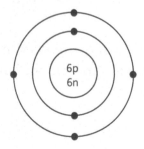

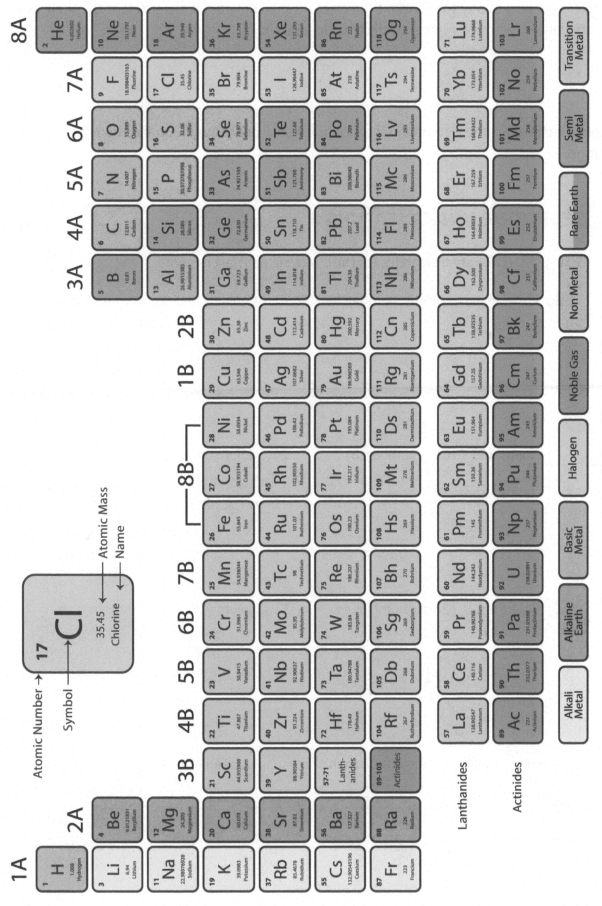

Figure 3.1 The Periodic Table of the Elements

© ollomy/Shutterstock.com. Adapted by Kendall Hunt Publishing.

A simpler and quicker way to represent the electron shell diagram is to represent the shells with short arcs labeled with the number of electrons (e^-) they hold:

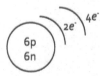

Valence electrons are the electrons in the outermost shell only; thus, neutral carbon has 4 valence electrons.

TEST YOUR UNDERSTANDING

?

1. Draw electron shell diagrams for the following neutral elements:

   A) Hydrogen (H), Atomic number: 1

   B) Beryllium (Be), Atomic number: 4

   C) Oxygen (O), Atomic number: 8

   D) Sodium (Na), Atomic number: 11

   E) Chlorine (Cl), Atomic number: 17

   F) Calcium (Ca), Atomic number: 20

2. How many valence electrons do each of these neutral elements have?

   H _1_   Be _2_   O _6_   Na _1_   Cl _7_   Ca _2_

Elements behave in ways that increase their stability. An atom is most **stable** when its valence shell is full of electrons. For many elements this means having eight electrons in the outermost shell, this is known as the **octet rule**. However, some elements may be stable having the first shell full with only two electrons.

To achieve stability, an element may either gain or lose valence electrons to form an ion. **Ions** are elements (and some molecules) that carry a charge due to a difference in the number of protons and electrons. Positively-charged ions are called **cations** and negatively-charged ions are called **anions**.

Ions are most often formed when one element takes electrons away from another element. In this way, both elements achieve stability. The resulting oppositely-charged cations and anions are then bonded to each other by an electrostatic attraction, forming an **ionic bond**.

For example, sodium (Na) easily donates its one valence electron to chlorine (Cl) (Fig. 3.2). Since Na lost one electron it now has a net charge of +1 and we write its *ionic form* as **Na⁺**, the sodium ion. Since Cl gained one electron it now has a net charge of –1 and we write its *ionic form* as **Cl⁻**, the chloride ion. These ions then form an ionic bond to create the *ionic compound* sodium chloride, NaCl (aka table salt).

Ionic Bonding of Sodium Chloride

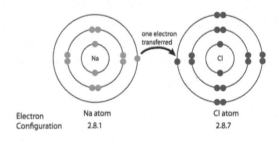

one electron transferred

| Electron Configuration | Na atom 2.8.1 | Cl atom 2.8.7 |

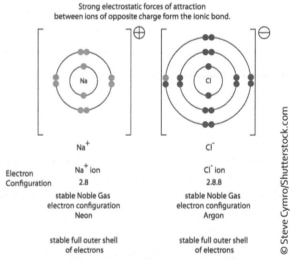

Strong electrostatic forces of attraction between ions of opposite charge form the ionic bond.

| Electron Configuration | Na⁺ ion 2.8 | Cl⁻ ion 2.8.8 |

stable Noble Gas electron configuration Neon

stable Noble Gas electron configuration Argon

stable full outer shell of electrons

stable full outer shell of electrons

© Steve Cymro/Shutterstock.com

Figure 3.2 Ionic bonding between sodium (Na) and chlorine (Cl) atoms.

APPLY YOUR UNDERSTANDING

?

Look back at your electron shell diagrams.

1. To achieve stability Beryllium will lose __2__ (how many?) electrons to form a __Cation +__ (cation or anion?).

What is the ionic form of Beryllium? __Be⁺²__

2. Oxygen will gain __2__ (how many?) electrons to form a __anion__ (cation or anion?).

What is the ionic form of oxygen? __O²⁻__

3. What is the ionic form of Potassium (K, #19)? __K⁺¹__

Elements can also achieve stability by sharing electrons with other atoms to form **molecules**. Each pair of shared electrons is a **covalent bond**. Many elements will form multiple covalent bonds to reach a stable, noble gas (Fig. 3.1, column 8A) configuration.

For example, recall that carbon has four valence electrons; carbon will form four covalent bonds giving it a full octet (8 valence electrons) like the stable gas neon. Hydrogen, with its one valence electron, will form only one covalent bond to fill its valence shell like helium. When brought together, one carbon atom will share its four valence electrons with four hydrogen atoms to make CH_4, methane gas (Fig. 3.3a). Each pair of shared electrons is a **single covalent bond** represented by a short dash between atoms in the **structural formula** of a molecule (Fig. 3.3b).

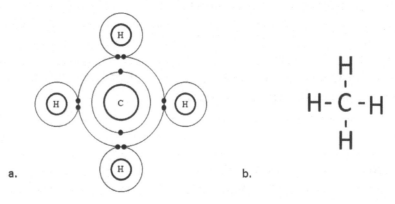

a.

b.

Figure 3.3 **Structure of CH_4, methane gas.** a) Hydrogen (H) and carbon (C) share valence electrons to give each atom a stable configuration. b) Methane's structural formula; pairs of shared valence electrons are drawn as single covalent bonds. Source: Damon Ely

---

? TEST YOUR UNDERSTANDING

1. How many covalent bonds will each of the following elements form?

   Hydrogen __1__   Oxygen __2__   Nitrogen __5__   Carbon __4__

2. Draw structural formulas for the following molecules:

   H_2O NH_3 CH_3OH

   H   H   H — C — H
                                           H

   H   :N: H
                    5 + 3 = 8
   H   (8)   full shell

Elements can also share two or three pairs of electrons to form **double and triple covalent bonds,** respectively. These are much stronger bonds represented by 2 or 3 dashes (Fig. 3.4). For example, the earth's atmosphere is made up of 21% oxygen gas (O_2) and 78% nitrogen gas (N_2). Oxygen and nitrogen atoms make two and three covalent bonds, respectively, to achieve an octet configuration. Thus, two oxygen atoms will form a double covalent bond to create O_2, and two nitrogen atoms will form a triple covalent bond to create N_2 (Fig. 3.4).

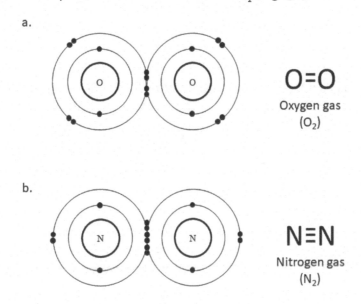

Figure 3.4   Electron shell diagram and structural formula for a) oxygen gas, and b) nitrogen gas. Source: Damon Ely

STRUCTURAL FORMULAS

Follow the steps below to help you determine the correct structural formula for each molecule.

a. Use only single bonds to start.
b. Bond all carbons together in a straight chain.
c. Add any N atoms to the carbon chain, then add any O atoms to the carbon chain.
d. Add hydrogens last since they can only form one bond.
e. Use double and triple bonds last to satisfy any elements that are missing bonds.
f. Look for clues in the writing of the molecular formula to help you.

1. Ethane, C_2H_6 2. Methanol, CH_3OH 3. Ethene, C_2H_4

4. Acetylene, C_2H_2 5. Ethyl alcohol, C_2H_5OH 6. Methylamine, CH_3NH_2

7. Acetic acid, CH_3COOH 8. Acetaldehyde, CH_3CHO 9. Cyanogen, C_2N_2

3.4 ACIDS, BASES, AND PH

To begin to understand concepts of pH, acids, and bases, we must first understand the *self-ionization* of the water molecule:

$$\textit{Self-ionization of water:} \quad \underset{\text{water}}{H_2O} \quad \rightarrow \quad \underset{\substack{\text{hydrogen} \\ \text{ion}}}{H^+} \quad + \quad \underset{\substack{\text{hydroxide} \\ \text{ion}}}{OH^-}$$

Whenever a water molecule dissociates in this way, it creates one **hydrogen ion, H^+,** and one **hydroxide ion, OH^-,** meaning these ions are always of equal concentration in pure water. Solutions that have equal amounts of these ions are called **neutral** solutions. **Acids** are molecules that increase the amount of H^+ when added to a solution while **bases** remove H^+ from solution, often by increasing the OH^- concentration.

TEST YOUR UNDERSTANDING

For each of the following molecules, write the two ions that will form in solution:

Example: Hydrochloric acid, HCl, is an acid because the hydrogen and chloride atoms ionize in solution to form H^+ and Cl^-.

Acids

Hydrofluoric acid, HF

$$HF \rightarrow H^{+1}-F^{-1}$$

Nitric acid, HNO_3

$$HNO_3 \rightarrow H^{+1}-N^{-1}-O^{-3}$$

Sulfuric acid, H_2SO_4

$$H^{+3}SO_4^{-2}$$

Bases

Sodium hydroxide
NaOH

$$Na^+ \; OH^+$$

Potassium hydroxide
KOH

$$K^- \; OH^+$$

Magnesium hydroxide
$Mg(OH)_2$

$$Mg^- \; OH^-$$

THE pH SCALE

Along with temperature, pH (a measure of acidity/alkalinity) is critical toward the maintenance of homeostasis in an organism. For example, blood plasma must be kept at a pH range from 7.32–7.42. This is because the enzymes that run the chemical reactions inside the cell are negatively affected when pH (and temperature) is not in an optimal range for their performance. You have many physiological mechanisms that monitor and make corrections to pH when changes occur.

The **pH scale** is a logarithmic scale of hydrogen ion (H^+) concentration (Fig. 3.5). Because the actual H^+ concentrations are exceedingly small and span many orders of magnitude, we mathematically transform the concentrations using a negative logarithm, which means the following: 1) lower pH values represent *greater* H^+ concentrations (more acidic), and 2) a change in one pH unit represents a 10-fold difference in H^+ concentration. Thus, a solution with pH 3 has a H^+ concentration 100 times greater than a solution with pH 5.

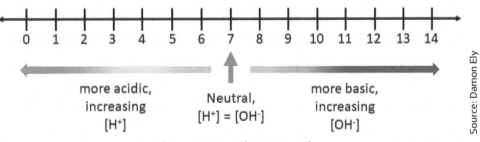

Figure 3.5　The pH scale.

APPLY YOUR UNDERSTANDING

1 Which is more acidic, lemon juice (pH2) or tomato juice (pH4)? _Lemon_

2. True or False: A solution with pH 10 has a greater H⁺ concentration than a solution with pH7. _F_

3. Soap has a pH of 10, making it mildly (acidic, neutral, or basic?) _basic_.

4. Coffee (pH_6) has a H⁺ concentration _10000_ times greater than soap (pH10).

5. A solution with pH7 has a H⁺ concentration _equal_ _to_ (greater than, less than, or equal to) its OH⁻ concentration.

Measure the pH of Common Solutions

Exercise 1

Before you begin, write down your predictions in Table 3.1 for each of the common solutions using the following descriptions: **strongly acidic, mildly acidic, neutral, mildly basic,** or **strongly basic**. Then use pH test strips or a pH meter to measure pH in each solution. Record the data in Table 3.1 along with your conclusion (strongly acidic, etc.).

Table 3.1   pH of Common Solutions.

Solution	Prediction	Measured pH Value	Conclusion
Tap water	6.5	5	
Soda	6.7		
Apple juice	6		
Soapy water	12	6	
Bleach solution	14	7	
Coffee	5	5	

APPLY: Tooth enamel begins to dissolve below pH 5.5. Underlying the enamel is dentin, the substance that makes up the bulk of a tooth's size, which dissolves below a pH of 6.5.

Based on your findings in Table 3.1, why might a dentist warn parents against giving their kids fruit juice as a healthy alternative to soda, even if the juice is sugar-free?

_____

_____

Measure the pH of Unknown Solutions

Exercise 2

Five solutions, A through E, of unknown pH have been prepared for you. You will use pH test strips, a pH meter, and two chemical indicator solutions to evaluate the pH of each unknown. Follow the procedure outlined below.

⚠ **WARNING:** Always wear gloves and eye protection when handling chemicals. Prevent cross-contamination of solutions by keeping dedicated pipettes with their solution bottles, and never submerge the pipette tip in any other solution. Do not put your own measuring or transfer device (dropper, pipette, etc.) into the stock bottle.

Procedure:

1. Obtain one of the unknown solutions labeled A, B, C, D, or E.
2. Use a pipette to place 5 drops of the unknown solution in each of two test tubes.
3. Fill ¼ of a third test tube with the unknown solution, immerse the probe of a pH meter and let it sit as you continue to work.
4. Use a pipette to place a drop of the unknown solution onto a pH test strip over a small dish.
5. In one of the test tubes from step 2, add 2 drops of bromothymol blue indicator solution. Swirl the tube gently and record the final color of the unknown solution in Table 3.2.
6. In the remaining test tube with the unknown solution, add 2 drops of phenolphthalein indicator solution. Swirl the tube gently and record the final color of the unknown solution in Table 3.2.
7. Record the pH meter reading in Table 3.2, along with the pH value obtained from using the color chart that accompanies the pH test strip. Rinse the pH meter probe in distilled water.
8. Repeat steps 1–7 until you have tested all five unknown solutions. Clean your test tubes, rinse the pH meter probe, dispose of used test strips and gloves, and clean your work area.
9. Your instructor may have you share your group's data with the class.

Table 3.2   pH of Unknown Solutions Using Different Methods.

Solution	Color after adding bromothymol blue	Color after adding phenolphthalein	pH Test Strip	pH meter
A				
B				
C				
D				
E				

ANALYZE YOUR RESULTS

1. Place the letter of each unknown solution over its pH value on the pH scale.

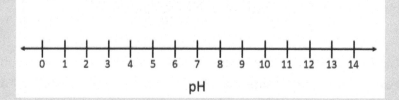

2. Which indicator solution is better for indicating . . .

basic solutions? _____ acidic solutions? _____

3. Look at the class data: Which method provided more **accurate** data, the <u>pH test strips</u> or the <u>pH meter</u>?

4. Look at the class data: Which method provided more **precise** data, the <u>pH test strips</u> or the <u>pH meter</u>?

5. Look at the class data: Each solution was tested multiple times by each group, meaning that each test was well-replicated.

- Are the replicate measurements of a solution more variable for some methods? If so, which ones?

- One reason for replicating a study is to account for any natural variation that may occur. However, our replicates were obtained from measuring the exact same bottle of solution, which has only one specific pH.

  For each method, *list some possible reasons* we might obtain variable results:

  o   pH Test Strips:

  o   pH Meter:

  o   Indicator Solution:

Chemical reactions occur when the elements within molecules interact in ways that result in new combinations of elements, thus creating new molecules. While some reactions occur spontaneously, most biological reactions require a small initial input of energy. These reactions are conducted by enzyme catalysts, which lower the energy barriers and speed up the reaction time.

You have already observed chemical reactions taking place by the change in color of certain indicator solutions. What are some other ways you could detect whether a chemical reaction happened or not? Take a moment to generate a list:

_____   _____

_____   _____

_____   _____

BALANCING CHEMICAL REACTIONS

Chemical reactions are written to show the number and identity of the molecules involved in the reaction, called the **reactants,** and of the **products** that are formed. For example, photosynthesis combines the reactants carbon dioxide (CO_2) and water (H_2O) to form the products glucose ($C_6H_{12}O_6$) and oxygen gas (O_2) in the following reaction:

$$\textit{Photosynthesis:} \quad \underbrace{6CO_2 + 6H_2O}_{\text{Reactants}} \rightarrow \underbrace{C_6H_{12}O_6 + 6O_2}_{\text{Products}}$$

The large numbers tell you how many of each molecule is present in the reaction (e.g., there are 6 molecules of CO_2), which is important for balancing the reaction. A reaction must be **balanced,** meaning all the elements on the reactants side must also appear in the products. In this example, there are 6 carbon atoms, 18 oxygen atoms, and 12 hydrogen atoms in both the reactants and the products, making it a balanced reaction.

? TEST YOUR UNDERSTANDING

Balance the following reactions by identifying the correct number of reactants and products.

__NaBr + __Cl_2 → __NaCl + __Br_2 __CH_4 + __O_2 → __CO_2 + __H_2O

__Al + __O_2 → __Al_2O_3 __$SiCl_4$ + __H_2O → __SiO_2 + __HCl

__C_2H_6 + __O_2 → __H_2O + __CO_2 __H_3PO_4 + __HCl → __PCl_5 + __H_2O

__N_2 + __O_2 + __H_2O → __HNO_3 __C_2H_6O + __O_2 → __CO_2 + __H_2O

Observe Chemical Reactions

You will perform the following two chemical reactions. Watch the reaction closely and write down any observations. Wear protective gloves and safety glasses.

Reaction #1: $NaCl + AgNO_3 \rightarrow NaNO_3 + AgCl$

Procedure:

1. Place 5 drops of 0.1M silver nitrate ($AgNO_3$) solution into a clean test tube.

2. Add 5 drops of 0.1M sodium chloride (NaCl) solution to the test tube and gently swirl.

    •   What did you observe when you added the NaCl?

    _____

    •   Write the names of the products that formed:

Sodium chloride + Silver nitrate → _____   +   _____

Reaction #2: $HCl + NaHCO_3 \rightarrow CO_2 + $ _____ + _____

Procedure:

1. Use a scoopula to place a small amount of sodium bicarbonate ($NaHCO_3$) onto a watch glass.

2. Add 5 drops of dilute hydrochloric acid solution (HCl) to the watch glass.

    •   What did you observe when you added the HCl?

    _____

    •   In addition to creating carbon dioxide (CO_2) gas, two other products are formed. Determine what those products must be by accounting for all the elements that appear in the reactants. <u>Write the molecular formulas for these two products in the blank spaces in the above reaction.</u>

CHAPTER 4
FACTORS THAT AFFECT ENZYME ACTIVITY

 Laboratory Objectives

By the end of this laboratory, the student should be able to:

- describe how enzymes carry out reactions using the terms activation energy, active site, substrate, and products;
- understand why enzymes have optimal ranges of environmental conditions in which they are most active;
- explain the design of the enzyme activity experiment and recognize aspects of proper scientific experimentation;
- provide explanations for the observed results of the experiment based on an understanding of how enzymes function.

Enzymes are proteins that organisms use to conduct biochemical reactions. Many processes performed by the cell, such as cellular respiration in the mitochondria of eukaryotic cells and photosynthesis in the chloroplasts of plant cells, are complex biochemical pathways composed of multiple steps—each of which is a separate reaction performed by a different enzyme. Thus, enzymes are essential to homeostasis because they are responsible for all the life-sustaining chemical reactions (collectively called *metabolism*) within an organism.

In this lab, you will learn how enzymes perform reactions, and your group will investigate some of the factors that affect an enzyme's activity (i.e., its ability to create products). You and your group will conduct an experiment to test how changes in temperature, pH, and the concentration of the enzyme itself influences the formation of products by the enzyme *catalase*.

An **enzyme** is a type of protein, one of the four groups of organic molecules (i.e., carbohydrates, lipids, proteins and nucleic acids) that play numerous structural and functional roles in organisms. Enzymes are molecules made by the cell that act as organic catalysts. A **catalyst** is an element or molecule that makes a reaction proceed more quickly but is not itself changed in any way.

ACTIVATION ENERGY

Enzymes speed up reactions by lowering the activation energy required for a reaction to proceed (Fig. 4.1). **Activation energy** is the amount of energy that must be put into a reaction before products can form. The activation energy serves as a barrier to the spontaneous interaction of reactants to form products. For example, gasoline and oxygen gas react explosively, but only when an initial input of energy (i.e., a spark) is provided; otherwise, gasoline can sit openly exposed to the oxygen gas in the air without reacting.

If the amount of activation energy is lowered, then it takes less time to meet the energy demand and begin forming products. Thus, enzymes greatly accelerate reaction speed, often by many orders of magnitude, allowing cells to more quickly digest large molecules, destroy foreign invaders, repair damage, and build new cell parts.

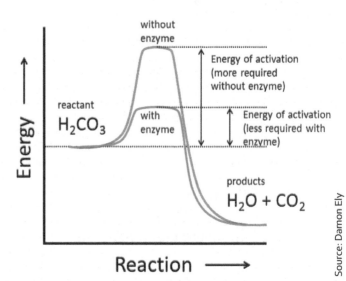

Figure 4.1   Activation energy. *Carbonic anhydrase* (an enzyme) lowers the activation energy of a reaction it catalyzes in the blood to convert the reactant, carbonic acid (H_2CO_3), to water (H_2O) and carbon dioxide gas (CO_2) products. Carbon dioxide then diffuses into the lungs to be exhaled.

ENZYMATIC ACTION

Enzymes are large macromolecules that fold into complex shapes which allow them to perform as catalysts. Because of this complexity, each enzyme has a uniquely-shaped **active site**, a region of the enzyme that attracts the **substrate** (i.e., the reactant) (Fig. 4.2). The substrate is said to fit perfectly into the active site like a key into a lock, meaning that each enzyme is specialized to carry out only one reaction. Like the reaction you will investigate, Fig. 4.2 shows an enzyme binding a single substrate molecule and splitting it into two separate products. Enzymes do not undergo any change themselves, allowing them to run the same reaction repeatedly.

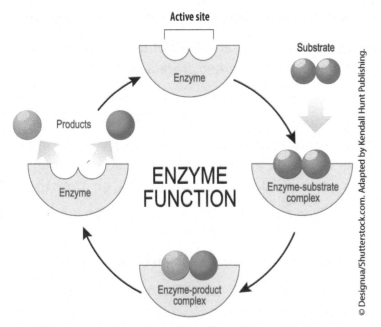

Active site

Enzyme

Substrate

Products

ENZYME
FUNCTION

Enzyme

Enzyme-substrate
complex

Enzyme-product
complex

© Designua/Shutterstock.com. Adapted by Kendall Hunt Publishing.

Figure 4.2 Enzymatic action. Enzymes have a uniquely-shaped active site that binds substrates forming an enzyme-substrate complex. After the products are released, an enzyme is ready to catalyze another reaction.

Enzymes have variable properties. Some enzymes carry out irreversible reactions while others can run reactions both forwards and backwards. Some active sites can attract substrates by having hydrophobic properties, while others may have a slight charge or hold a metallic element at its center. Many enzymes can bind more than one substrate at once. Some enzymes have their active sites covered up and remain inactive until conditions change and their active site is exposed.

Enzymes do not carry out reactions similarly in different environmental conditions. Changes in pressure, temperature, pH, and salt concentration can all affect an enzyme's activity by altering its structure and changing the shape of its active site, a process known as **denaturation**. Without a perfectly-shaped active site to fit its substrate, an enzyme cannot function. Different enzymes have different optimal ranges in certain environmental conditions; for example, enzymes of the stomach can only function in very low pH solutions, they denature when they enter the higher pH of the small intestine where other enzymes function best.

4.2 INVESTIGATION: FACTORS AFFECTING ENZYME ACTIVITY

You will investigate the following reaction:

$$H_2O_2 \xrightarrow{\text{catalase}} H_2O \;+\; O_2$$

hydrogen
peroxide

water

oxygen
gas

The enzyme **catalase** is important to most organisms because it converts harmful hydrogen peroxide, a natural by-product of certain cellular reactions, to harmless water and oxygen gas products. Your class will expose solutions of catalase and hydrogen peroxide to different levels of enzyme concentration, pH and temperature, and measure the production of oxygen gas to find the optimal range of catalase activity within each condition.

Factors Affecting Enzyme Activity: Enzyme Concentration, pH, and Temperature

Your instructor may ask your group to perform some or all of the following experiments. Be aware that the instructor may modify certain procedures.

WARNING: Always wear gloves and eye protection when handling chemicals. Prevent cross-contamination of solutions by keeping dedicated pipettes with their solution bottles, and never submerge the pipette tip in any other solution. Do not put your own measuring or transfer device (dropper, pipette, etc.) into the stock bottle.

Preparation of Catalase Solution (your instructor may have already completed this step)

1. Cut ½ a large potato into small pieces and place into blender with 500 mL of distilled water.
2. Blend on high for 30 seconds.
3. Pour mixture through cheese cloth or a sieve to remove pulp.
4. Use immediately.

EXPERIMENT 1: EFFECT OF ENZYME CONCENTRATION

Materials:

12 narrow test tubes	catalase solution	hand ruler	stopwatch
12 wide test tubes	distilled water	wax pencil	pipettes

Overview: You will measure oxygen gas production after adding hydrogen peroxide to test tubes containing different amounts of the catalase enzyme. Each enzyme concentration will be replicated three times.

Question: How does the amount of enzyme present in a solution affect the amount of product formed?

State a predictive hypothesis: _____

_____

Procedure (read through the procedures before starting the experiment):

1. <u>1x enzyme concentration</u>: Designate 3 narrow test tubes as 1a, 1b, and 1c. Use the hand ruler and wax pencil to mark the following distances up from the bottom of these test tubes: 0.5 cm and 8.0 cm. Fill with catalase to the 0.5 cm mark, then add distilled water to the 8.0 cm mark.
2. <u>2x enzyme concentration</u>: Designate 3 narrow test tubes as 2a, 2b, and 2c. Use the hand ruler and wax pencil to mark the following distances up from the bottom of these test tubes: 1.0 cm and 8.0 cm. Fill with catalase to the 1.0 cm mark, then add distilled water to the 8.0 cm mark.

3. <u>3x enzyme concentration</u>: Designate 3 narrow test tubes as 3a, 3b, and 3c. Use the hand ruler and wax pencil to mark the following distances up from the bottom of these test tubes: 1.5 cm and 8.0 cm. Fill with catalase to the 1.5 cm mark, then add distilled water to the 8.0 cm mark.

4. <u>4x enzyme concentration</u>: Designate 3 narrow test tubes as 4a, 4b, and 4c. Use the hand ruler and wax pencil to mark the following distances up from the bottom of these test tubes: 2.0 cm and 8.0 cm. Fill with catalase to the 2.0 cm mark, then add distilled water to the 8.0 cm mark.

5. Prepare a stopwatch for each set of three tubes. Be prepared to move through the remaining steps quickly.

6. Add hydrogen peroxide (H_2O_2) to test tubes 1a, 1b, and 1c until completely full.

7. As soon as each test tube is filled, another group member should immediately place a wide test tube completely over the narrow tube and invert (turn upside-down). Place the inverted tube back in the test tube rack.

8. When all three test tubes are inverted, start the stopwatch and immediately measure the initial headspace (in cm) by measuring the distance from the top of the inverted narrow test tube down to the liquid surface. Record the initial headspace in Table 4.1.

9. Repeat steps 6 through 8 for the remaining three groups of test tubes.

10. Measure the headspace in each test tube after 5, 10, 15, and 20 minutes. Record the data in Table 4.1.

11. For each test tube at the end of the experiment, correct your data by subtracting the initial headspace measurement from each of the 5, 10, 15, and 20-minute readings. Enter the corrected values in Table 4.1.

12. Clean your workspace; rinse all test tubes and leave them to dry in the test tube racks.

Table 4.1   Effect of enzyme concentration: measurements of headspace (cm) over time.

Enzyme Concentration		Initial headspace (cm)	Headspace (cm) after 5 min (actual / - initial)	Headspace (cm) after 10 min (actual / - initial)	Headspace (cm) after 15 min (actual / - initial)	Headspace (cm) after 20 min (actual / - initial)
1X:	1a		/	/	/	/
	1b		/	/	/	/
	1c		/	/	/	/
2X:	2a		/	/	/	/
	2b		/	/	/	/
	2c		/	/	/	/
3X:	3a		/	/	/	/
	3b		/	/	/	/
	3c		/	/	/	/
4X:	4a		/	/	/	/
	4b		/	/	/	/
	4c		/	/	/	/

EXPERIMENT 2: EFFECT OF PH

Materials:

15 narrow test tubes	catalase solution	hand ruler	pH buffers: 3, 5, 7, and 9	pipettes
15 wide test tubes	distilled water	wax pencil	1M NaOH solution	stopwatch

Overview: You will measure oxygen gas production after adding hydrogen peroxide to test tubes containing the catalase enzyme in solutions of differing pH. Each pH treatment will be replicated three times.

Question: How does pH affect the amount of product formed in an enzyme-catalyzed reaction?

State a predictive hypothesis: _____

_____

Procedure (read through the procedures before starting the experiment):

1. <u>pH 3</u>: Designate 3 narrow test tubes as 1a, 1b, and 1c. Use the hand ruler and wax pencil to mark the following distances up from the bottom of these test tubes: 1.0 cm and 8.0 cm. Fill with catalase to the 1.0 cm mark, then add pH 3 buffer to the 8.0 cm mark.
2. <u>pH 5</u>: Designate 3 narrow test tubes as 2a, 2b, and 2c. Use the hand ruler and wax pencil to mark the following distances up from the bottom of these test tubes: 1.0 cm and 8.0 cm. Fill with catalase to the 1.0 cm mark, then add pH 5 buffer to the 8.0 cm mark.
3. <u>pH 7</u>: Designate 3 narrow test tubes as 3a, 3b, and 3c. Use the hand ruler and wax pencil to mark the following distances up from the bottom of these test tubes: 1.0 cm and 8.0 cm. Fill with catalase to the 1.0 cm mark, then add pH 7 buffer to the 8.0 cm mark.
4. <u>pH 9</u>: Designate 3 narrow test tubes as 4a, 4b, and 4c. Use the hand ruler and wax pencil to mark the following distances up from the bottom of these test tubes: 1.0 cm and 8.0 cm. Fill with catalase to the 1.0 cm mark, then add pH 9 buffer to the 8.0 cm mark.
5. <u>pH 14</u>: Designate 3 narrow test tubes as 5a, 5b, and 5c. Use the hand ruler and wax pencil to mark the following distances up from the bottom of these test tubes: 1.0 cm, 7.0 cm, and 8.0 cm. Fill with catalase to the 1.0 cm mark. Add distilled water to the 7.0 cm mark, then add 1M NaOH to the 8.0 cm mark.
6. <u>Let all test tubes sit for three minutes to allow the catalase to acclimate to the pH.</u>
7. Prepare a stopwatch for each set of three tubes. Be prepared to move through the remaining steps quickly.
8. Add hydrogen peroxide (H_2O_2) to test tubes 1a, 1b, and 1c until completely full.
9. As soon as each test tube is filled, another group member should immediately place a wide test tube completely over the narrow tube and invert (turn upside-down). Place the inverted tube back in the test tube rack.
10. When all three test tubes are inverted, start the stopwatch and immediately measure the initial headspace (in cm) by measuring the distance from the top of the inverted narrow test tube down to the liquid surface. Record the initial headspace in Table 4.2.

11. Repeat steps 8 through 10 for the remaining four groups of test tubes.
12. Measure the headspace in each test tube after 5, 10, 15, and 20 minutes. Record the data in Table 4.2.
13. For each test tube at the end of the experiment, correct your data by subtracting the initial headspace measurement from each of the 5, 10, 15, and 20-minute readings. Enter the corrected values in Table 4.2.
14. Clean your workspace; rinse all test tubes and leave them to dry in the test tube racks.

Table 4.2   Effect of pH: measurements of headspace (cm) over time.

pH of Solution		Initial headspace (cm)	Headspace (cm) after 5 min (actual / - initial)	Headspace (cm) after 10 min (actual / - initial)	Headspace (cm) after 15 min (actual / - initial)	Headspace (cm) after 20 min (actual / - initial)
pH 3:	1a		/	/	/	/
	1b		/	/	/	/
	1c		/	/	/	/
pH 5:	2a		/	/	/	/
	2b		/	/	/	/
	2c		/	/	/	/
pH 7:	3a		/	/	/	/
	3b		/	/	/	/
	3c		/	/	/	/
pH 9:	4a		/	/	/	/
	4b		/	/	/	/
	4c		/	/	/	/
pH 14:	5a		/	/	/	/
	5b		/	/	/	/
	5c		/	/	/	/

EXPERIMENT 3: EFFECT OF TEMPERATURE

Materials:

12 narrow test tubes	catalase solution	hand ruler	stopwatch	warm water bath (40°C)
12 wide test tubes	distilled water	wax pencil	ice bath (4°C)	boiling water bath (100°C)
pipettes				

Overview: You will measure oxygen gas production after adding hydrogen peroxide to test tubes containing the catalase enzyme in solutions of differing temperature. Each temperature treatment will be replicated three times.

Question: How does temperature affect the amount of product formed in an enzyme-catalyzed reaction?

State a predictive hypothesis: _____

_____

Procedure (read through the procedures before starting the experiment):

1. Ice bath (4°C): Designate 3 narrow test tubes as 1a, 1b, and 1c. Use the hand ruler and wax pencil to mark the following distances up from the bottom of these test tubes: 1.0 cm and 8.0 cm. Fill with catalase to the 1.0 cm mark, then add distilled water to the 8.0 cm mark. Place these three tubes in the ice bath for 5 minutes to acclimate to the new temperature.

2. Room temperature (25°C): Designate 3 narrow test tubes as 2a, 2b, and 2c. Use the hand ruler and wax pencil to mark the following distances up from the bottom of these test tubes: 1.0 cm and 8.0 cm. Fill with catalase to the 1.0 cm mark, then add distilled water to the 8.0 cm mark. Place these three tubes in the test tube rack on your lab table.

3. Warm water bath (40°C): Designate 3 narrow test tubes as 3a, 3b, and 3c. Use the hand ruler and wax pencil to mark the following distances up from the bottom of these test tubes: 1.0 cm and 8.0 cm. Fill with catalase to the 1.0 cm mark, then add distilled water to the 8.0 cm mark. Place these three test tubes in the warm water bath for 5 minutes to acclimate.

4. Boiling water bath (100°C): Designate 3 narrow test tubes as 4a, 4b, and 4c. Use the hand ruler and wax pencil to mark the following distances up from the bottom of these test tubes: 1.0 cm and 8.0 cm. Fill with catalase to the 1.0 cm mark, then add distilled water to the 8.0 cm mark. Place these three test tubes in the boiling water bath for 5 minutes, then carefully remove them using a test tube holder and allow them to cool for 3 minutes before continuing.

5. Prepare a stopwatch for each set of three tubes. Be prepared to move through the remaining steps quickly.

6. Add hydrogen peroxide (H_2O_2) to test tubes 1a, 1b, and 1c until completely full.

7. As soon as each test tube is filled, another group member should immediately place a wide test tube completely over the narrow tube and invert (turn upside-down). Place the inverted tubes back in the ice bath (see * in step 9).

8. When all three test tubes are inverted, start the stopwatch and immediately measure the initial headspace (in cm) by measuring the distance from the top of the inverted narrow test tube down to the liquid surface. Record the initial headspace in Table 4.3.

9. Repeat steps 6 through 8 for the remaining three groups of test tubes. *The room temperature tubes and the boiling water bath tubes will be completed at your lab table. Ice bath tubes and warm water bath tubes should always be in their baths for the duration of the experiment.

10. Measure the headspace in each test tube after 5, 10, 15, and 20 minutes. Record the data in Table 4.3.

11. For each test tube at the end of the experiment, correct your data by subtracting the initial headspace measurement from each of the 5, 10, 15, and 20-minute readings. Enter the corrected values in Table 4.3 ("- initial").

12. Clean your workspace; rinse all test tubes and leave them to dry in the test tube racks.

Table 4.3   Effect of temperature: measurements of headspace (cm) over time.

Temperature	Initial headspace (cm)	Headspace (cm) after 5 min (actual / - initial)	Headspace (cm) after 10 min (actual / - initial)	Headspace (cm) after 15 min (actual / - initial)	Headspace (cm) after 20 min (actual / - initial)
4°C: 1a					
1b					
1c					
25°C: 2a					
2b					
2c					
40°C: 3a					
3b					
3c					
100°C: 4a					
4b					
4c					

DATA ANALYSIS

Begin your data analysis by calculating the *average headspace* for each group of three replicates using the corrected data values in Table 4.3. Enter those data in Tables 4.4, 4.5, and 4.6. Each average should be reported to one decimal place. Do not include test tubes with known errors (check with your instructor). In addition, calculate the difference in headspace (Δ *headspace*) for each 5-minute interval.

Table 4.4   Effect of enzyme concentration. Average headspace (cm) over time calculated from 3 replicate trials within each level of enzyme concentration.

Enzyme Concentration	Average headspace (cm) after 5 min	Average headspace (cm) after 10 min	Δ *headspace* (10 min – 5 min)	Average headspace (cm) after 15 min	Δ *headspace* (15 min – 10 min)	Average headspace (cm) after 20 min	Δ *headspace* (20 min – 15 min)
1x							
2x							
3x							
4x							

Table 4.5   Effect of pH. Average headspace (cm) over time calculated from 3 replicate trials within each level of pH.

pH	Average headspace (cm) after 5 min	Average headspace (cm) after 10 min	Δ *headspace* (10 min – 5 min)	Average headspace (cm) after 15 min	Δ *headspace* (15 min – 10 min)	Average headspace (cm) after 20 min	Δ *headspace* (20 min – 15 min)
3							
5							
7							
9							
14 (NaOH)							

Table 4.6 Effect of temperature. Average headspace (cm) over time calculated from 3 replicate trials within each level of temperature.

Temperature (°C)	Average headspace (cm) after 5 min	Average headspace (cm) after 10 min	Δ headspace (10 min – 5 min)	Average headspace (cm) after 15 min	Δ headspace (15 min – 10 min)	Average headspace (cm) after 20 min	Δ headspace (20 min – 15 min)
4							
25							
40							
100							

Exercise 2

Data Analysis: Construct Line Graphs of Headspace Over Time

Use the following three blank graphs to plot the data from Tables 4.4, 4.5, and 4.6. Each graph should contain a separate line for each level of the treatment. For example, the graph for the effect of pH should contain 5 lines—one for each pH level. Be sure to clearly label each line (e.g., "pH 3", "4°C", etc. . . .), and label each axis with the correct variable; choose scales that maximize the use of the graph area. Note: the Δ *headspace* data will be used later in the results and should not be used for any of the line graphs.

Line Graph 1—Effect of Enzyme Concentration

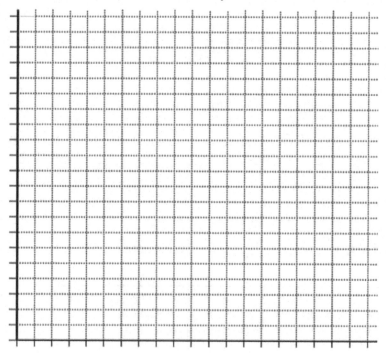

Line Graph 2—Effect of pH

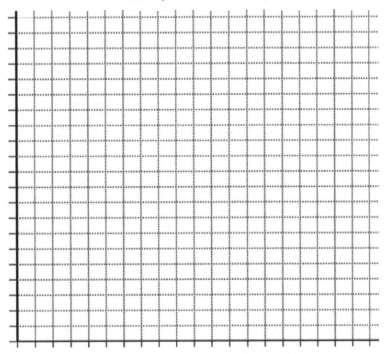

Line Graph 3   Effect of Temperature

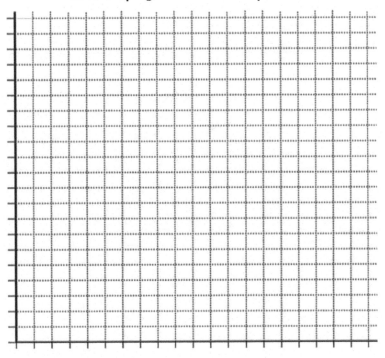

Data Analysis: Construct Bar Graphs of Final Headspace

Exercise 3

Use the following three blank graphs to create bar graphs showing only *the final average headspace* (i.e., the 20-minute data only) for each level within a treatment. Again, choose your labels and axis scales carefully; make the widths of your bars equal to 3 or 4 tick marks.

Bar Graph 1—Effect of Enzyme Concentration

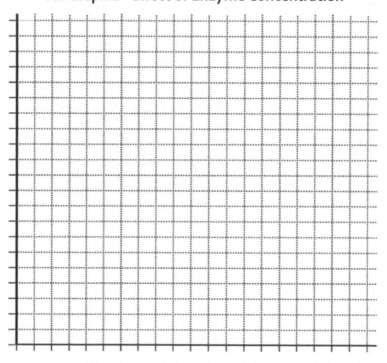

Bar Graph 2—Effect of pH

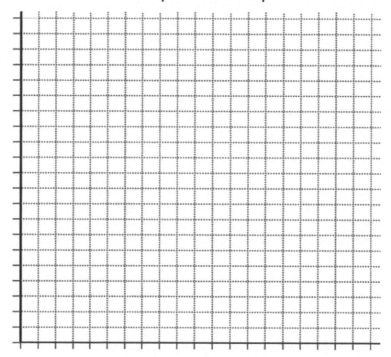

Bar Graph 3—Effect of Temperature

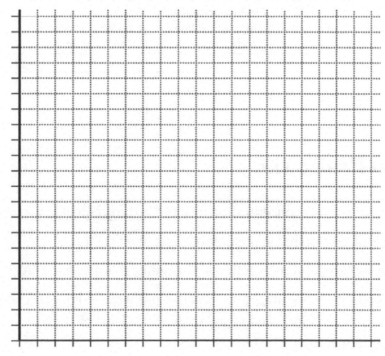

Exercise 4

Data Analysis: Determine the Rate of Enzyme Activity Over Time

Calculate rates of product formation over the course of the reaction for each level of each treatment. Start by dividing the average 5-min headspace measurements in Tables 4.4, 4.5, and 4.6 by 5 to obtain a cm/min rate of product formation for the first 5 minutes of the experiment. Then do the same using the Δ *headspace* calculations in Tables 4.4, 4.5, and 4.6 to calculate rates for each subsequent 5-minute period.

Table 4.7   Effect of enzyme concentration on rates of product formation.

Enzyme Concentration	Production rate (cm/min) between 0 and 5 minutes	Production rate (cm/min) between 5 and 10 minutes	Production rate (cm/min) between 10 and 15 minutes	Production rate (cm/min) between 15 and 20 minutes
1x				
2x				
3x				
4x				

Table 4.8   Effect of pH on rates of product formation.

pH	Production rate (cm/min) between 0 and 5 minutes	Production rate (cm/min) between 5 and 10 minutes	Production rate (cm/min) between 10 and 15 minutes	Production rate (cm/min) between 15 and 20 minutes
3				
5				
7				
9				
14 (NaOH)				

Table 4.9   Effect of temperature on rates of product formation.

Temperature (°C)	Production rate (cm/min) between 0 and 5 minutes	Production rate (cm/min) between 5 and 10 minutes	Production rate (cm/min) between 10 and 15 minutes	Production rate (cm/min) between 15 and 20 minutes
4				
25				
40				
100				

INTERPRET THE DATA

?

1. Which level of enzyme concentration resulted in the greatest enzyme activity? _____

2. Which level of pH resulted in the greatest enzyme activity? _____

3. Which level of temperature resulted in the greatest enzyme activity? _____

4. Which graphs, the line graphs or the bar graphs, would you choose to use in a presentation to more quickly and easily show which level of each treatment resulted in the greatest enzyme activity?

5. The line graphs provide more information than the bar graphs. Do the line graphs show any trends over the experiment that might either contradict or call into question the results displayed by the bar graphs? Explain for each treatment.

Enzyme concentration:

pH:

Temperature:

6. Look over the rates of product formation. Are rates generally highest during the beginning, middle, or end of the reaction?

7. We often observe that reaction rates slow down towards the end of the reaction; this is reflected as a 'plateau' in the line graph. Is this what you observed? What would cause the formation of the product to plateau over time? (Recall that a certain amount of substrate was provided, and that one of the products was a gas that escapes solution.)

8. Describe some of the possible sources of error in this experiment.

APPLY YOUR UNDERSTANDING

Your lab instructor may ask you to provide thorough answers to the following questions as part of an assignment or laboratory report.

1. Why are enzymes necessary for all organisms? Provide a clear rationale and use two specific examples of enzyme-driven reactions in cellular processes to support your answer. (*Hint: Think about the various organelles in a cell.*)

2. Think carefully about the details of your experimental design.

   a. Why did we replicate each test? In other words, what is the reason scientists incorporate *replication* into the design of any experiment?

   b. In what specific way did we prepare the test tubes to ensure that any difference in O_2 production between two different tests (e.g., pH 3 vs. pH 7) would be due *only* to the independent variable (e.g., pH)? Compare two specific test tubes from this experiment to illustrate your point.

3. Use the vocabulary associated with enzyme-catalyzed reactions to explain what caused O_2 production (i.e., headspace distance) to change the way it did when enzyme concentration increased.

APPLY: Dr. Mycelia studies different types of bread mold and she finds that one kind of mold consistently breaks down bread faster than all the others. State a possible hypothesis Dr. Mycelia may offer to explain this observation.

4. Explain why enzyme activity changed substantially as the pH moved farther away from neutral conditions.

APPLY: Dr. Salmo conducts a study comparing the metabolic rates of fish, which are driven by the fishes' enzymes, in acidic versus neutral streams. How might our lab experiment help him explain any differences he finds in fish metabolism between these two types of streams?

5. Explain why enzyme activity changed the way it did as conditions changed a) from the ice bath to room temperature, and b) from room temperature to the boiling water treatment.

APPLY: Dr. Borrelia discovers a species of bacteria living under sea ice where temperatures are so extremely low that no other organisms exist. She wants to know why their physiology allows them to survive and function in this harsh environment. How might our lab experiment help her decide what to focus on as she begins to investigate?

CHAPTER 5
THE COMPOUND MICROSCOPE

 Laboratory Objectives

By the end of this laboratory, the student should be able to:

- identify the parts of a compound microscope;
- define the terms *field of view*, *depth of field*, *plane of focus*, *resolving power*, and *parfocal capability*;
- calculate the total magnification of an object;
- properly position a glass slide and use the microscope to center and focus on a specimen;
- prepare a wet mount.

The microscope is one of the most important pieces of equipment used by biologists. Since cells are typically less than 100 micrometers (0.1 millimeters) in length, a microscope is necessary to examine the shape and organization of cells in biological tissues. The great magnifying power and resolution provided by microscopes make them standard equipment in most biological and medical laboratories.

Some microscopes, like the **scanning electron microscope (SEM)**, have incredibly high magnification levels and resolving power. The SEM, which fires a beam of electrons at a sample and detects returning signals from the atoms within the sample, can magnify objects up to 500,000 times—creating detailed images of the most minute features of cells. However, the high cost of the SEM prohibits their general use in most laboratories.

Light microscopes use a light source to view specimens typically up to a 1000x magnification level. Two types of light microscopes are commonly used: the **dissecting microscope** (aka the stereomicroscope), and the **compound microscope**. Dissecting microscopes have lower magnification power but allow the observer to view larger objects like small animals, plants, and rocks. The compound microscope allows much higher magnification levels, but the specimen must be extremely thin and mounted on a glass slide. This laboratory will give you practical experience using the compound microscope to view specimens quickly and easily.

Exercise 1

Identify the parts of the compound microscope

Obtain a compound light microscope from the cabinet as instructed and bring it back to your table. *ALWAYS USE BOTH HANDS WHEN TRANSPORTING A MICROSCOPE.* One hand should support the **base** while the other grips the **arm** (Fig. 5.1). Use Fig. 5.1 to become familiar with the parts of your microscope and use the information below to learn how these parts function.

1. The **ocular lenses** (or, oculars) are the eyepieces that you look through. Your microscope is most likely *binocular*, meaning that there are two ocular lenses. These lenses have a magnification power of 10x and can be adjusted to the width of your eyes. Depending on the model of your microscope, either one or both oculars can be focused to suit each of your eyes. Most microscopes have a pointer, a thin black needle, in one ocular that can be used to point out a feature of the specimen to another observer.

2. The **objective lenses** provide magnification and resolution of the specimen. The multiple objective lenses (described below) may be moved into position by rotating the **revolving nosepiece** until the desired objective lens snaps into place. Each of the objective lenses has a different name, and each provides a different level of magnification printed on the side of the lens. The exact magnification of each lens can vary depending on the manufacturer; the magnifications listed here are most common.

   The **scanning lens** provides 4x magnification and is used first to bring the specimen into focus and to locate areas of interest that you wish to observe at higher magnification. *It is good practice to always have the scanning lens in position before you begin and when you are finished.*

   The **low-power lens** provides 10x magnification, and the **high-power lens** provides either 40x or 45x magnification. You will likely use the low-power lens to view most specimens; the high-power lens is most useful when examining the features of individual cells is required.

   The **oil immersion lens** provides 100x magnification and requires a drop of specialized oil to bridge between the surface of the slide and the lens. The oil bridge reduces the refraction of light that occurs as light passes from the glass slide to the air, a phenomenon that only becomes noticeable at high magnification. *You will not need to use the oil immersion lens to view the specimens in your laboratory and care should be taken not to put this lens into position.*

3. The **stage** is the platform on which the glass slide is held by an apparatus called the **mechanical stage**. The mechanical stage allows the observer to move the slide forward, backward, and sideways using the **stage adjustment knobs**.

4. Underneath the stage is the **condenser**, which focuses a beam of light up through the stage and the specimen. The condenser ensures an even spread of light over the specimen. The amount of light passing through the condenser can be adjusted using the **iris diaphragm**.

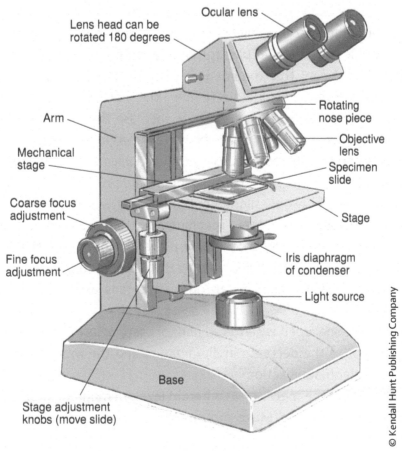

Ocular lens

Lens head can be
rotated 180 degrees

Arm

Mechanical
stage

Coarse focus
adjustment

Fine focus
adjustment

Rotating
nose piece

Objective
lens

Specimen
slide

Stage

Iris diaphragm
of condenser

Light source

Base

Stage adjustment
knobs (move slide)

© Kendall Hunt Publishing Company

Figure 5.1   The Compound Microscope.

5.   The **coarse and fine focus knobs** are located on the lower part of the arm. The smaller fine focus knob is nested within the larger coarse focus knob. The coarse focus should be used at lower magnifications only, for even slight adjustments of the coarse focus at higher magnifications (i.e., while using the high-power lens) will easily blur the image. Likewise, the fine focus should never be used at lower magnifications. Rotating the fine focus knob through numerous revolutions is not only tedious (when only a slight adjustment of the coarse focus is required), but it wears out the inner mechanism, damaging the microscope over time.

5.2 USING THE COMPOUND MICROSCOPE

Exercise
2

View the "letter e" slide

Obtain a slide from your instructor that contains a small, printed letter *e*. Make sure the scanning lens is in position and use the mechanical stage to secure the slide. Turn the power switch on and make sure that the light source is working properly. Then, do the following:

1.   First, using your naked eye, make sure that the specimen is centered over the beam of light coming up through the stage. Adjust the distance between the oculars to the width of your eyes.

2. Look through the oculars and turn the coarse focus knob until the letter *e* comes into view; adjust the brightness to your level of comfort. Notice that the *e* appears upside-down and backwards. This is due to the passage of light through both the objective lens and the ocular lens. This means that the image will appear to travel the opposite direction when you use the stage adjustment knobs to move the slide.

3. Once the specimen is in focus, prepare to increase the magnification by first centering the part of the specimen you wish to examine more closely. *These steps (center and focus) should always be done before increasing the magnification*. When you are ready, turn the rotating nosepiece to place the low-power lens into position.

4. Notice that the *e* is now only slightly out of focus, this is a demonstration of the **parfocal capability** of the objective lenses—meaning that the image remains mostly in focus when changing magnification. You should only need to slightly adjust the fine focus knob to create a sharp image. What happened to the illumination, or level of brightness, when you increased magnification? What kinds of details are you able to notice at higher magnification?

5. Making sure the specimen is centered and focused, rotate the high-power lens into position. Again, notice the decrease in illumination and the more-detailed features you can observe at higher magnification.

6. Continue to look at the specimen at different levels of magnification until you feel comfortable using the microscope. Make sure the scanning lens is in position before you remove the slide.

TOTAL MAGNIFICATION

You know that each objective lens has its own level of magnification, but when you look through the microscope you are looking through two lenses—the objectives and the oculars. Recall that the oculars have their own magnification of 10x. The **total magnification** is the product (not the sum) of the magnification of both lenses.

CHECK YOUR UNDERSTANDING

Determine the total magnification when using the different objective lenses. Remember, the magnification is printed on each objective lens.

Objective lens	Objective magnification	Ocular magnification	Total magnification (objective x ocular)
Scanning lens	4x	10x	40x
Low-power lens	10x	10	100x
High-power lens	40	10x	400x
Oil immersion lens	100	10x	1,000x

Recall that before you increase the magnification it is very important to make sure the area of the slide you wish to observe is centered. This is because the total visible area, known as the **field of view**, decreases with increasing magnification (Fig. 5.2). If the area of interest is not centered when you increase magnification, there is a good chance it won't be in your field of view. Instead of searching for the lost item of interest, which may take a considerable amount of time, it is best to lower the magnification and begin again.

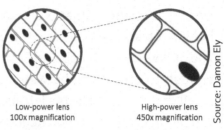

Low-power lens
100x magnification

High-power lens
450x magnification

Source: Damon Ely

Figure 5.2 Field of view. Under a higher-power lens the area you are viewing becomes smaller.

Another phenomenon associated with increasing magnification is a shallower depth of field. **Depth of field** refers to the thickness of the layer that is in the **plane of focus**. For example, when viewing a single-celled organism under low magnification (e.g., when using the scanning lens) there will be only one point in which it appears to be in focus (i.e., the plane of focus is relatively thick). However, when the magnification is increased you will be able to focus on the organism at multiple levels as you continue to turn the focus knob (Fig. 5.3). In this case, the depth of field is so shallow that there are several thin planes of focus throughout the specimen.

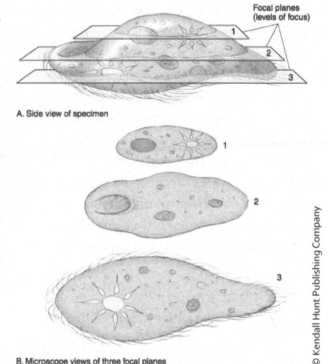

Focal planes
(levels of focus)

A. Side view of specimen

B. Microscope views of three focal planes

© Kendall Hunt Publishing Company

Figure 5.3 Plane of focus. At higher magnification the depth of field becomes shallower, allowing you to view multiple levels within a specimen.

Exercise
3

Observe Depth of Field

Obtain a slide that contains three overlapping colored threads.

View the point where the threads intersect at different magnifications; start with the scanning lens.

Under the scanning lens, are you able to determine which thread is on top? _____

Under higher power, try to determine the order of the threads by focusing up and down:

Color of top thread: _____ Middle thread: _____ Bottom thread: _____

Complete the statement: The depth of field under higher magnification is _____ (<u>greater</u> or <u>less</u>?) than the depth of field under lower magnification.

Have you ever wondered why microscopes are so expensive? This is due in part to the high resolving power of the objective lenses. **Resolving power** is the ability to distinguish between two closely adjacent images. For example, imagine using your phone to take a picture of someone holding up an open book on the other side of a large room. You could zoom in on the picture, but you still wouldn't be able to read the book because the resolving power of the lens is not great enough to distinguish between the separate letters on the page. Similarly, adjacent cells are so small that they are like the letters on the page—only a high-quality lens with great resolving power can provide the resolution needed to tell them apart.

MAKING A WET MOUNT SLIDE

Many of the slides you will view in the laboratory are "fixed" slides created using an adhesive to permanently seal the specimen under a coverslip for many years of use. However, it is possible to create a temporary slide of a freshly-collected specimen called a **wet mount slide** (Fig. 5.4). The specimen is placed in a drop of water on the slide and covered with a **coverslip,** a small transparent piece of glass or plastic that provides a flat surface for unobstructed viewing.

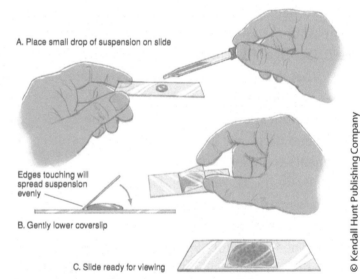

A. Place small drop of suspension on slide

Edges touching will spread suspension evenly

B. Gently lower coverslip

C. Slide ready for viewing

© Kendall Hunt Publishing Company

Figure 5.4   Making a wet mount slide.

Exercise 4

Make a Wet Mount Slide

Your instructor will provide a sample of pond water containing many small living organisms for you to view by making a wet mount slide. Follow the procedure below and refer to Fig. 5.4 for help.

1. Obtain a clean glass slide and coverslip.
2. Use a pipette to collect a small amount of pond water and squeeze one or two drops onto the glass slide.
3. Carefully place one edge of the coverslip on the slide and contact the water.
4. Gently lower the coverslip, evenly spreading the water under the coverslip. This prevents any trapped air bubbles from obstructing your view.
5. Practice your skills with the microscope by searching for organisms and viewing them at different magnification levels.

CHAPTER 6
CELL STRUCTURE AND FUNCTION

 Laboratory Objectives

By the end of this laboratory, the student should be able to:

- identify the differences between prokaryotic and eukaryotic cells;
- list the various organelles found in eukaryotic cells and describe their functions;
- recognize common protists and understand how fungi function;
- identify the differences between plant and animal cells;
- use the microscope to view individual cells and identify their features.

The cell is the smallest unit of life. Some organisms, like bacteria and many protists, are only composed of one single cell and referred to as **unicellular**. Many other forms of life, like plants and animals, are **multicellular** organisms composed of trillions of cells. In multicellular organisms, cells group together to form specialized tissues, organs, and organ systems that work in unison to maintain **homeostasis**—a constant internal state of life-sustaining conditions that is characteristic of all living things.

In addition to homeostasis, all living things share common characteristics such as the ability to grow and reproduce, respond to stimuli, adapt to their surroundings, and acquire materials and use energy. However, the differences among organisms are many—from their differing appearances and behaviors all the way down to their cellular characteristics.

In this laboratory, you will become familiar with the two general types of cells we find in organisms—prokaryotic and eukaryotic cells—and the structure and function of the various organelles we find in eukaryotic cells. In addition, you will gain experience making wet mounts of plant and animal tissues to view individual cells under the compound microscope.

All organisms on Earth are composed of one or more cells. All cells have a **cell membrane** composed of a *phospholipid bilayer* that surrounds the **cytoplasm**—the contents of the cell. Other features shared by all cells include **DNA**, the genetic material, and **ribosomes** to produce proteins. We recognize two broad categories of organisms, prokaryotes and eukaryotes, depending upon the types of cells they possess.

PROKARYOTES

Prokaryotic cells are relatively small and simple, and all prokaryotes are single-celled organisms. The prokaryotes consist of two major Domains of life: The Bacteria and the Archaea. Archaea are like bacteria in many ways but are more closely related to eukaryotes. We will use bacteria to represent the prokaryotes (Fig. 6.1).

Prokaryotic cells lack many of the complex features found in eukaryotic cells. In prokaryotic cells, the DNA—the genetic material—is simply condensed into a central region known as the **nucleoid**. Throughout the cytoplasm **ribosomes**, which can be thought of as small molecular machines, use the information from DNA to synthesize the proteins necessary for homeostasis. Prokaryotic cells frequently have one or more long whip-like **flagella** that they use for locomotion. They are also frequently covered by shorter *pili* (sometimes called fimbriae) that serve various purposes, including attachment to surfaces and exchange of genetic material with other bacteria. In addition, many bacteria produce outer protective layers including a **cell wall** (different from the cell wall of plant cells) and a *capsule*.

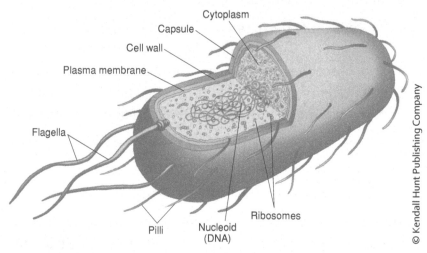

© Kendall Hunt Publishing Company

Figure 6.1   A bacterium, a prokaryotic cell.

Exercise 1

Observe Prokaryotic Cell Structure

Locate the model of a bacterium on display. Use Fig. 6.1 and the descriptions above to locate the following structures on the model. Check off each structure you observe.

__ *Cell Membrane*   __ *Cytoplasm*   __ *Cell wall*   __*Nucleoid*

__ *Flagellum*   __ *Pili*   __ *Ribosomes*

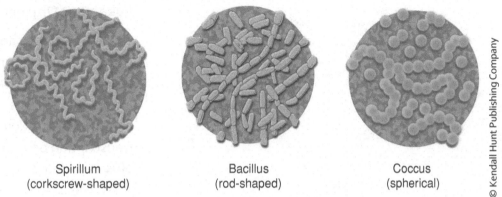

| Spirillum (corkscrew-shaped) | Bacillus (rod-shaped) | Coccus (spherical) |

© Kendall Hunt Publishing Company

Figure 6.2   Three types of bacteria.

Bacterial cells have different morphologies, or shapes, that help us to classify them. In general, three different forms are recognized: the rod-shaped **bacillus**, the spherical **coccus**, and the corkscrew-shaped **spirillum** (Fig. 6.2). Recognizing these forms is an important first step for medical professionals to diagnose different diseases. For example, *Helicobacter pylori*, the spirillum bacterium that causes peptic ulcers, is easily recognizable by its corkscrew shape.

Exercise 2

Observe Bacteria Types

View a slide showing three bacteria types under a compound microscope. You will need to increase magnification to the high-power lens. Move through the entire slide and familiarize yourself with the appearance of spirillum, bacillus, and coccus bacteria.

EUKARYOTES

Eukaryotic cells belong to a domain of life called Eukarya and include the following **kingdoms** of life: Protista, Plantae, Fungi, and Animalia. Eukaryotic cells are much larger and more complex than those of prokaryotes, and most eukaryotes are multicellular (most protists and some fungi are single-celled). The defining feature of eukaryotic cells is the presence of a **nucleus**, the organelle that holds DNA—the genetic material.

Organelles are specialized structures found only within eukaryotic cells. Organelles carry out highly-specific functions, allowing eukaryotes to spend less time and energy on cellular processes, making them more efficient. Most organelles are membrane-bound compartments filled with enzymes; the specificity of an organelle is due to these enzymes, which conduct a common set of complicated reactions to carry out a certain function (e.g., photosynthesis in the chloroplasts of plant cells).

Exercise 3

Learn About the Organelles

Fig. 6.3 shows the organelles and other features common to animal and plant cells. Find the models of these cells on display in the lab and familiarize yourself with these features. Then, use the descriptions of the various organelles to help you learn the role played by each of them in eukaryotic cells.

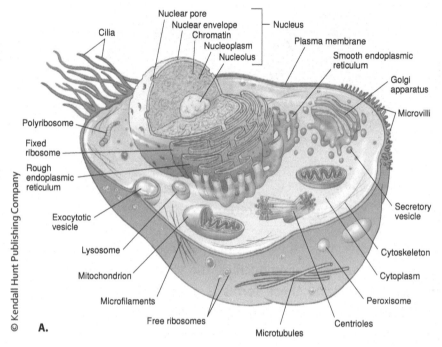

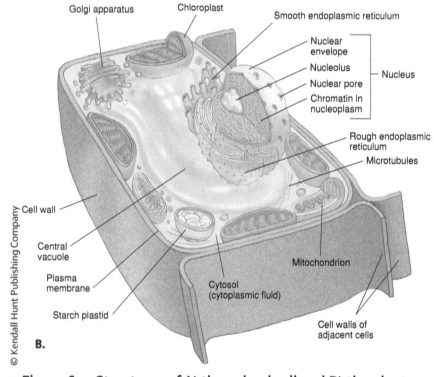

Eukaryotic Organelles

1. The **nucleus** holds DNA within a double membrane called the **nuclear envelope**. Inside the nucleus processes like DNA replication and DNA transcription occur. The **nucleolus** is a dense region inside the nucleus where ribosomes are created.

2. The **rough endoplasmic reticulum**, or **rough ER**, is an extension of the nuclear membrane arranged into a series of flattened sacs covered with ribosomes, giving it a rough appearance. The rough ER is where the cell makes most proteins.

3. The **smooth ER** are membranous, tubular compartments that construct lipids, process carbohydrates, detoxify the cell, and are also used to store calcium.

4. The **Golgi apparatus** is a series of flattened sacs containing enzymes that sort the newly-formed molecules coming from the ER. Once sorted, the Golgi directs the groups of similar molecules to their various destinations inside, or outside, the cell.

Figure 6.3 Structures of A) the animal cell and B) the plant cell.

5. **Transport vesicles** are membrane-bound capsules that carry molecules from one organelle to another.

6. **Lysosomes** are vesicles that contain hydrolytic enzymes used to break down obsolete cell parts or incoming substances. **Peroxisomes** are like lysosomes except their function is more specific: to break down the long fatty acid chains of triglycerides.

7. **Mitochondria** are responsible for the creation of adenosine triphosphate (ATP), the molecule used by cells as a source of energy. The creation of ATP is through a series of reactions called *cellular respiration*, which combines simple sugars with oxygen to produce ATP and the waste molecule CO_2.

8. **Chloroplasts** are the organelles responsible for *photosynthesis* in plant cells. Each chloroplast is filled with tiny, disc-shaped structures called *thylakoids* that contain chlorophyll, the pigment that gathers sunlight energy. Chloroplasts produce glucose, which is used by the mitochondria to make ATP, and they also produce O_2 gas as a by-product of photosynthesis.

9. The **cytoskeleton** refers to a few different types of long fibrous proteins that help to support the structure of the cell and its organelles, and some are responsible for cellular movement. Actin filaments (aka microfilaments) and microtubules are two different kinds of cytoskeleton fibers.

10. A large **central vacuole** is present in most plant cells, and in some protists (kingdom Protista). The vacuole in plants fills with water and serves to provide the plant cell with turgor pressure, pushing the cell membrane up against the cell wall to help expand growing cells, extend the leaves, and support the plant's upright position. When a plant needs water its vacuole empties and the cell membrane pulls away from the cell wall, a process called *plasmolysis*, causing the plant to wilt. In protists, vacuoles store ingested food particles, regulate water content, and eject waste materials.

In addition to organelles, eukaryotic cells have various surface features. The **cell wall** of plant cells is an external layer composed of cellulose and various other substances. The cell wall prevents excess water from entering and bursting the cell and is reinforced by strong fibers that give wood its rigid structure. Some eukaryotic cells have **flagella** (e.g., sperm cells) while others are coated with short hair-like structures called **cilia**. Some cells have a cell membrane that is folded into small ridges called **microvilli** which greatly increase the surface area to enhance the efficiency of certain processes.

CHECK YOUR UNDERSTANDING

(?)

1. Complete the table to identify the differences between prokaryotic and eukaryotic cells:

Cell Type	Groups of organisms	Relative size	Simple or complex?	Possess a nucleus?	Possess other organelles?	Single-celled or mostly multicellular?
Prokaryotic	bacilly bacteria/ protist	smaller	simple	nucleoid	yes	singe
Eukaryotic	multicellular plants, fungi	larger		yes	yes	multi

2. List all the features that differ between plant and animal cells in the following chart:

Plant cell	Animal cell
- Cell wall - chloroplasts - large vacuole - Mitocondria	No cell wall Does not have chloroplast - centrioles - some have large vacuoles

3. For each of the following descriptions, identify the appropriate organelle.

- This organelle would be used by a white blood cell to destroy foreign invaders like bacteria.

  lysosomes

- This organelle would be found in great abundance inside muscle cells, which require lots of energy to contract.

  Mitocondria

- This organelle would be used by the cell to make new phospholipids for the cell membrane.

  ER

- This organelle must dissolve to let the chromosomes (DNA) move to either side of the cell before cell division.

  ~~Vaco~~   ~~Nucleus~~   centrioles

- This organelle would be found in cells of the leaves of plants but not the roots.

  chloroplasts

- A cell in the salivary gland would use this organelle to make the enzyme salivary amylase (i.e., a protein).

  rough ER   ~~golgi apparatus~~

- The salivary gland cell would use this organelle to gather all the amylase enzymes together and give them directions on where to go.

  ~~vacuole~~   ER eticulum

- This organelle in the salivary gland cell would then carry the amylase enzymes to the cell membrane and deposit them outside the cell to join the saliva.

  transport vesicle

The following exercises will familiarize you with the characteristics of various eukaryotic cells. In addition to learning about a few common aquatic protists, you will observe some structural features of a common fungus (bread mold), plant cells, and animal cells.

Observe Common Protists

Exercise 4

Find the compound microscopes in the laboratory containing the slides of the following aquatic protists: *Spirogyra*, *Paramecium*, and *Euglena*. Observe these organisms and follow the instructions for each to learn about their characteristics. You may be instructed to make wet mount slides of living specimens.

SPIROGYRA

Spirogyra is a genus of freshwater algae consisting of cylindrical cells that attach to one another in long **filaments** (Fig. 6.4). In warm, nutrient-rich water *Spirogyra* can form thick, silky mats of hair-like strands on the surface. These mats are often interspersed with large quantities of oxygen-filled bubbles as a by-product of the photosynthetic process. There are over 400 species of *Spirogyra* currently recognized.

Spirogyra are easily recognized under the microscope because of the unique spiral arrangement of their **chloroplasts**. The chloroplasts, which contain CO_2-gathering centers called *pyrenoids*, encircle a large **central vacuole**. The **nucleus** is suspended within the vacuole by strands of cytoplasm that attach to the chloroplasts.

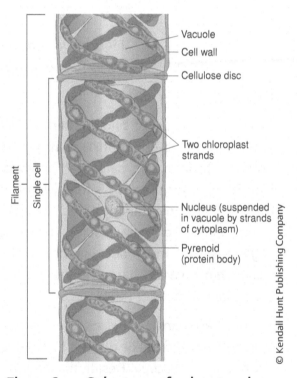

Vacuole
Cell wall
Cellulose disc
Two chloroplast strands
Nucleus (suspended in vacuole by strands of cytoplasm)
Pyrenoid (protein body)
Filament
Single cell

© Kendall Hunt Publishing Company

Figure 6.4 *Spirogyra*, a freshwater alga.

PARAMECIUM

Paramecium is a genus of single-celled freshwater protists that belong to a group broadly known as the ciliates, so named due to the many fine **cilia** that cover their outer surface (Fig. 6.5). Paramecium is abundant in all aquatic habitats and can be observed swimming in a tumbling, spiral motion caused by the beating of their cilia.

The distinct slipper-like shape of *Paramecium* is due to the presence of the **oral groove**, a cleft in the cell membrane used to direct small food particles to an internal oral cavity. Food particles are then enveloped by a **food vacuole** containing digestive enzymes. Other prominent features of the cell include **anterior and posterior contractile vacuoles** that expel excess water that enters through osmosis, and the appearance of two nuclei, a **macronucleus** and a **micronucleus**. The micronucleus contains genetic material that is exchanged with other cells in a reproductive process called *conjugation*.

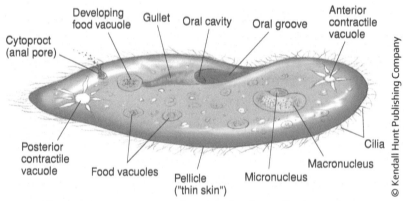

Figure 6.5 *Paramecium*, **a single-celled protist.**

EUGLENA

Euglena is a genus of single-celled, flagellated, photosynthetic protists that inhabit both freshwater and saltwater habitats. Like *Paramecium*, *Euglena* is free-living and can ingest organic food particles in a similar manner using food vacuoles. However, *Euglena* also carries out photosynthesis using **chloroplasts** that give the cell its green appearance.

The **flagellum** of *Euglena* is extremely long and thin and can be difficult to observe under the microscope. Beside the long flagellum is a second, shorter flagellum that does not protrude. A small, reddish **eyespot** can be found beside both flagella and is involved in *phototaxis*—the detection of light and subsequent movement towards the light source.

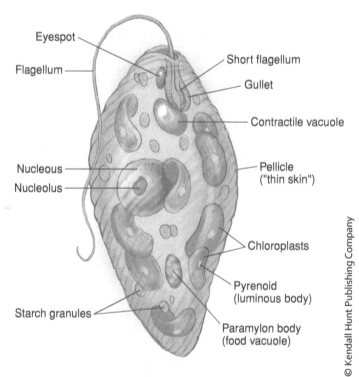

Figure 6.6 *Euglena*, **a single-celled photosynthetic protist.**

Another distinguishing characteristic of *Euglena* is the **pellicle**, a series of protein strips that wrap around the cell membrane. These strips (which are microtubules) can slide past one another, giving *Euglena* considerable flexibility and the ability to contract and expand.

Exercise 5

Observe the Bread Mold *Rhizopus*

Find the compound microscope containing the slide of *Rhizopus*—a common bread mold. Use Fig. 6.7 and the following information to identify the features of *Rhizopus* and learn about its biology.

RHIZOPUS

Rhizopus is a multicellular fungus that you have probably encountered in the form of mold on bread. *Rhizopus* is a *saprotroph*, meaning that it secretes digestive enzymes that hydrolyze the organic molecules of the substrate (bread, wood, etc.), creating individual monomers that are absorbed and used inside the fungal cells.

Saprotrophic fungi grow by extending thin filaments known as **hyphae** (singular: hypha or **stolon**) throughout the substrate. The hyphae secrete the digestive enzymes and they are anchored by short, root-like structures called **rhizoids**. Fungal reproduction is achieved by the creation of thousands of tiny **spores** (or, *sporangiospores*) that develop inside a capsule-like **sporangium** at the end of a long stalk called the **sporangiophore**. Spores are released into the air where they can travel long distances before colonizing a new substrate. When you see moldy bread, mushrooms, or the shelf fungi on tree trunks you are seeing only the reproductive portions of these fungi—the bulk of the fungal biomass lies within the substrate in the form of masses of hyphae called *mycelia*.

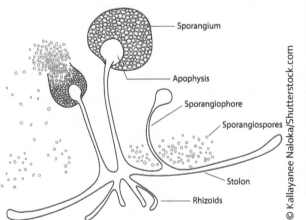
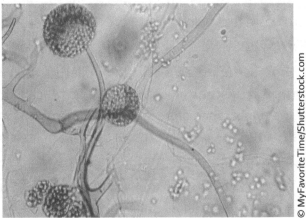

Figure 6.7 *Rhizopus*, **the common bread mold.**

Observe Plant Cells

Exercise 6

Specimens of *Elodea* (water weed) and *Allium* (onion) are available in the laboratory. Follow the guidance of your instructor and use the procedures below to make wet mounts of both specimens for observation under the compound microscope. Also, use the plant cell model available in the laboratory to help you identify some features.

ELODEA

Elodea is a genus of aquatic plant that grows entirely underwater. Its leaves are only 2 cell layers, making it ideal for observation of living plant cells.

Procedure:

1. Place a drop of distilled water on a clean glass slide.
2. Using a pair of forceps, carefully remove a single leaf from a main stalk of *Elodea* and place in the drop of water on your slide.
3. Touch one end of a coverslip to the drop of water and allow the coverslip to fall over the specimen as you previously learned.
4. Begin viewing the sample under the compound microscope using the scanning lens.

Observe the *Elodea* leaf under the scanning lens. Notice that the leaves of this species have a *serrulate margin*, meaning that the edges of the leaf have many small teeth pointing toward the tip.

Increase the magnification to observe individual cells. Notice the thick, rigid **cell wall** that surrounds each cell. The cell wall appears as a dark border that gives the cell a rectangular shape. Inside each cell are numerous **chloroplasts**. Some chloroplasts may appear to be moving in a circular motion around the periphery of the cell, an event known as **cytoplasmic streaming**. Cytoplasmic streaming is caused by the movement of motor proteins, which create currents in the cytoplasm that help to distribute materials around the cell. In this case, the chloroplasts are simply being carried around the cell by these currents.

Because of the density of chloroplasts within *Elodea* cells, the nucleus is often difficult to distinguish. A large **central vacuole** occupies each *Elodea* cell. The vacuole's presence can be detected by the appearance of a mostly clear, empty space at the center of most cells because, when filled with water, the vacuole presses the chloroplasts to the outside margins of the cell.

Sketch your field of view of *Elodea* under high-power magnification. Label your sketch using the terms in bold (above) and write down the total magnification.

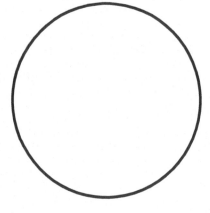

Sketch of *Elodea*

Total magnification = _____

ONION CELL (ALLIUM)

Allium is a genus of plants that includes onions, garlic, scallions, and many other species that are often used for cooking. These plants typically develop a large underground bulb composed mostly of water and the carbohydrate molecule starch. You will prepare a wet mount of a thin layer of onion bulb tissue and use iodine as a stain to observe the structure of onion cells.

Procedure:

1. Place a drop of distilled water on a clean glass slide.
2. Gently snap a small piece of onion in half using your fingers—a thin, semi-transparent film should appear to still hold the two halves together. Use forceps to carefully peel this thin layer of tissue off and place it on the drop of water as a single layer (try to avoid letting the tissue fold up on itself).
3. Add a single drop of iodine over the onion tissue and place a coverslip on top. Allow 2–3 minutes for the iodine to stain the cells.
4. Begin viewing the sample under the compound microscope using the scanning lens.

Observe the onion epidermal tissue under the scanning lens. Find a clear, unobstructed area in which to view the cells—focus, center, and increase the magnification. Observe the **cell walls** of the onion cells and notice that they do not appear as thick as those of *Elodea*, resulting in a less rigid cell structure. Notice how onion cells tend to have rounded, tapered ends as opposed to the rectangular, brick-like structure of *Elodea* cells. A **nucleus** should be visible within each onion cell, appearing beige or brown because of the iodine stain. Some cells' nuclei might have a visible **nucleolus**.

Sketch your field of view of the onion tissue under high-power magnification. Label the nucleus and cell walls of an onion cell and write down the total magnification.

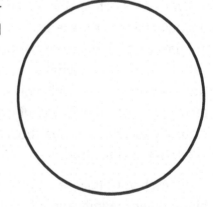

Sketch of onion epithelium tissue

Total magnification = _____

THINK FURTHER

1. Which organelles were easily observed in large numbers within *Elodea* cells but not in onion cells? Why not?

2. Onion cells do possess a large central vacuole. Why couldn't you find evidence of its presence?

Observe Animal Cells—Cheek Epithelium

Exercise 7

Follow the guidance of your instructor and use the procedures below to make a wet mount of epithelial cells from your inner cheek for observation under the compound microscope. Also, use the animal cell model available in the laboratory to aid you.

The inner lining of your mouth is composed of cells called simple squamous epithelium—these are cells that slough off easily, making them easy-to-obtain specimens for the observation of animal cells under the microscope.

Procedure:

1. Place a drop of the blue dye solution available in the laboratory on a clean glass slide.
2. Use a toothpick to gently scrape the inside surface of your cheek.
3. Dab the tip of the toothpick in the drop of blue dye to release the cells. Dispose the toothpick in the marked container. Do not place the toothpick in the trash.
4. Place a coverslip on top of the sample and begin viewing the sample under the compound microscope using the scanning lens.

Your cells will appear as small blue flake-like debris scattered around the viewing area. Find a small cluster of these cells to view under high magnification. Notice how the shape of these animals cells differs from the plant cells viewed previously. The absence of a cell wall in animal cells causes some animal cell types to appear round as opposed to rectangular. Also because of the absence of a cell wall, you are viewing the **cell membrane** of each cell; the cell membrane of *Elodea* and *Allium* cells was indistinguishable from the thick cell walls in those specimens. Finally, a centrally-located **nucleus** should be easily observable within each cell, appearing dark blue as a result of the stain used.

Sketch your field of view of your cheek epithelial cells under high-power magnification. Label the nucleus and cell membrane of the cells and write down the total magnification.

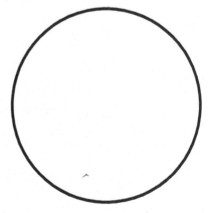

Sketch of cheek epithelial cells

Total magnification = _____

CHAPTER 7
CELL TRANSPORT: SIMPLE DIFFUSION AND OSMOSIS

 Laboratory Objectives

By the end of this laboratory, the student should be able to:

- describe how Brownian motion is evidence for the effects of random molecular movement;
- explain simple diffusion and understand its importance in biological systems;
- identify various factors that affect the rate of diffusion;
- explain osmosis and use the concept of tonicity to predict the direction of water movement;
- graph experimental data and use these data to determine if a solution is hypertonic, hypotonic, or isotonic.

Cell transport refers to the various ways in which cells move materials back and forth across the cell membrane. The resources needed by the cell to carry out basic functions must first cross the phospholipid bilayer of the cell membrane to gain entry. Likewise, the products and wastes to be secreted must also cross this hydrophobic barrier to exit. Some of these events happen on their own, without any energy or assistance needed by the cell itself, a phenomenon known as **passive transport**, while others require the cell to spend ATP energy and use transport proteins to aid the movement, which is known as **active transport**.

This laboratory exercise will focus on two types of passive (i.e., no energy required) transport: simple diffusion and osmosis. You will simulate these processes by creating artificial cells and altering the concentrations of solutes both inside and outside the cell. As you complete these activities, try to think about the importance of these processes to living cells; you will need to repeatedly recognize and apply the concepts of simple diffusion, osmosis, and active transport to the tissue and organ systems covered later in the course.

Atoms and molecules are always in motion. Even the molecules in a solid substance like a chair or a block of ice are constantly vibrating. In liquids and gases, atoms, ions, and molecules exhibit *translational motion*, the movement through space from one location to another, due to thermal energy. These movements are random in direction and occur at various speeds. Because they are objects with mass, atoms and molecules collide frequently, giving them new trajectories and speeds from moment to moment.

In 1827, a botanist named Robert Brown noticed that microscopic particles emitted from pollen grains were displaying erratic movements that were not life-related. Brown described his observations but he could not explain them. It was not until Albert Einstein published a paper in 1905 that the mechanism was known—Einstein explained that it was the constant collisions between the particles and the water molecules in solution that created the erratic motion that Brown had observed.

This phenomenon came to be known as **Brownian motion**, the random motion of particles suspended in a liquid or gas caused by collisions with other molecules. Fig. 7.1 shows how, like striking a cue ball through a table of billiards balls, the repeated collisions of a fast-moving molecule can cause the suspended particles to move in any direction.

Brownian motion

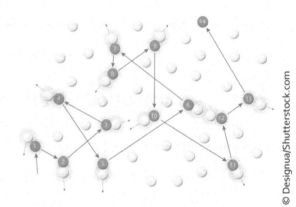

Figure 7.1   Brownian motion. The random motion of the white particles is caused by their collisions with the faster-moving red particle.

Observe Brownian Motion

Exercise 1

1. Place a small drop of diluted milk on a glass slide and cover the drop with a cover-slip.

2. View under a compound microscope; work your way up in magnification until you are viewing through the high-power lens.

3. You should be able to see many small droplets of fat suspended in the solution. Focus closely on some of the smallest droplets, which should appear to tremble or vibrate.

Your instructor may have prepared a microscope with oil immersion magnification for a better view of Brownian motion.

A **solution** is the combination of a **solvent**, typically water, and one or more dissolved **solutes**. If the concentration of solutes is higher in one area of a solution than another (i.e., there is a **concentration gradient**) Brownian motion will result in **simple diffusion**—the net directional movement of the solute from areas of higher solute concentration towards areas of lower solute concentration (Fig. 7.2). We describe the movement of the solute as moving *down the concentration gradient*. The *net* movement of the solute will stop when the solution reaches **equilibrium** and all areas are of equal concentration.

© gritsalak karalak/Shutterstock.com

Figure 7.2   Simple Diffusion.
A drop of red dye molecules (the solute) added to water (the solvent) will move from the area of higher concentration toward areas of lower concentration until equilibrium is reached and the concentration is the same throughout.

CHECK YOUR UNDERSTANDING

1. Simple diffusion is passive, meaning that no energy must be added to cause the directional movement of the solute. Explain the reason for this using Fig. 7.2, where the dye molecules naturally move towards areas of lower concentration.

_____

_____

2. Why do we say that the *net* movement of the solute stops at equilibrium? Have the solutes stopped moving completely? After equilibrium is reached, do you expect to once again see areas of the solution in Fig. 7.2 become higher or lower in solute concentration? Why or why not? Write a couple sentences that collectively answers these questions.

_____

_____

_____

How Does Molecular Weight Affect the Rate of Diffusion?

Exercise 2

Read the following information and answer the first three questions before you observe the results in the petri plate that is on display in the laboratory.

A petri dish filled with agar has been prepared by adding one drop of methylene blue (molecular weight = 374 g mole^{-1}) in one half of the plate, and one drop of potassium permanganate (molecular weight = 158 g mole^{-1}) in the other half. Both were left to diffuse for the same amount of time.

1. Which molecule do you predict will diffuse faster? _____

2. Why did you choose this molecule? _____

3. Complete the following explanatory hypothesis:

    Molecules diffuse at different rates because _____.

4. Observe the petri dish on display. Write down only the results you see in the dish, being careful not to interpret their meaning in your descriptions.

5. Which molecule moved faster? _____

    How can you tell, what is your evidence? Explain the connection between distance and time.

6. Think about all the molecules that our cells need like oxygen gas, glucose, and water, etc. How do you think the differences in diffusion rates have affected the timing and efficiency of cellular processes like cellular respiration in mitochondria, or photosynthesis in chloroplasts? Explain.

SEMIPERMEABLE MEMBRANES

Cells and organelles are surrounded by a membrane composed of phospholipid molecules arranged in a bilayer. Because the fatty acid tails of the phospholipids are **nonpolar**, they are **hydrophobic** and the two layers arrange inside the membrane tail-to-tail. Because the phosphate heads are **polar**, they are **hydrophilic** and face the aqueous extracellular space on the outside and the interior cytoplasm (Fig. 7.3).

The inner hydrophobic core of biological membranes makes them **semipermeable** (or *differentially permeable*) to various solutes, meaning that some solutes move more easily than others, and sometimes only if the cell allows the solute to cross.

You have already considered the role of size in the rate of diffusion, now consider how size will affect a molecule's ability to cross the cell membrane. In general, *smaller molecules move more easily across a semipermeable membrane* simply due to their ability to more easily slip between the large phospholipids.

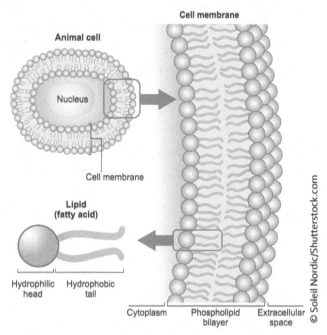

Figure 7.3 Structure of the cell membrane. The hydrophobic bilayer of cell membranes causes them to be differentially permeable to various solutes.

© Soleil Nordic/Shutterstock.com

Solutes must also be <u>*nonpolar*</u> *and* <u>*neutral*</u> *to easily cross the hydrophobic cell membrane.* This is because if a solute is a polar molecule or carries a charge, the nonpolar tails of the phospholipids will repel the substance. To move these solutes, cells must rely on transport proteins in a process known as **facilitated diffusion.** This form of transport involves a protein embedded in the cell membrane that allows some solutes that are large, polar, and/or charged to cross the cell membrane. The protein simply provides an opening that allows these solutes to pass according to their concentration gradient, meaning that facilitated diffusion is another passive form of transport.

❓ CHECK YOUR UNDERSTANDING

Which of the following solutes will easily cross a cell membrane (no protein or ATP required)? Describe why or why not beside each solute:

H_2O _____ CO_2 _____

O_2 _____ HCO_3^- _____

Na^+ _____   Starch _____

$C_6H_{12}O_6$ (glucose) _____

Exercise 3

Experiment: Simple Diffusion Across a Semipermeable Membrane

You will use dialysis tubing to create artificial cells to demonstrate simple diffusion. Your instructor may ask your group to do one or both of the following experiments. Follow the procedures as instructed; be sure to wear protective gloves and use caution when making solutions.

Dialysis tubing is made of cellulose fibers interweaved to create tiny molecular pores that allow small molecules to pass through them but block larger molecules. Since it is not a living membrane, dialysis tubing can only discriminate based on size, not on polarity or charge.

Procedure:

1. Fill two beakers with 200 mL of tap water. To one beaker add 10 drops of sodium hydroxide (NaOH). To the other beaker, add 20–40 drops of iodine. Place the beakers on labeled pieces of paper so you know which beaker has which solution.
2. Find the dialysis tubing for use in the laboratory. Obtain two pieces (approximately 15 cm in length) and soak the tubing in water before gently rubbing it between your fingers to form a hollow tube. You will use the tubing to create a small bag of solution.
3. Close one end of each bag by folding and twisting the tubing, then tying it tightly with a small piece of string.
4. Using a graduated cylinder, fill one bag with 10 mL of distilled water. Add 3 drops of phenolphthalein and place your bag in the beaker with the sodium hydroxide solution with the open end of the bag secured over the rim of the beaker with an elastic band (Fig. 7.4).
5. Fill the other bag with 10 mL of starch suspension and place this bag in the beaker with the iodine solution in the same way as Fig. 7.4.
6. Observe any changes in color in the contents of the bags. Answer the questions that follow.

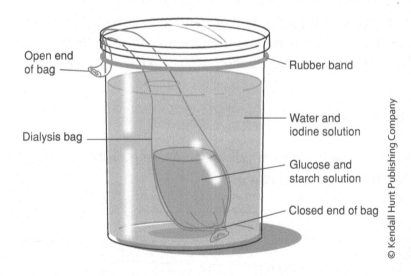

Open end of bag

Rubber band

Dialysis bag

Water and iodine solution

Glucose and starch solution

Closed end of bag

© Kendall Hunt Publishing Company

Figure 7.4 Experimental setup for simple diffusion. The bag of solution represents a cell surrounded by a semipermeable membrane.

ANALYZE THE RESULTS

Sodium Hydroxide/Phenolphthalein Experiment

1. Two ions form when sodium hydroxide, NaOH, is in solution. What are these two ions?

Na⁺   OH⁻

2. Considering these ions, will adding NaOH make the solution more acidic or more basic?

basic

3. Phenolphthalein is a very large organic molecule that turns pink in basic solutions. Will the phenolphthalein molecules be able to move down their concentration gradient and diffuse outside the bag? _NO_ Will the ions in the NaOH solution move down their concentration gradient and diffuse into the bag? _Yes_

4. Did you observe a color change outside the bag, inside the bag, or in both places?
_____

5. Use complete sentences to properly explain the results of this experiment using your understanding of simple diffusion and what you've learned from answering the previous questions.

Starch/Iodine Experiment

1. Molecular iodine (I_2) is two atoms of iodine connected by a covalent bond. Starch is a polysaccharide composed of hundreds of glucose monomers bonded together. Which of these two solutes, iodine or starch, will <u>not</u> be allowed by the membrane to move down its concentration gradient?

Starch

2. Iodine reacts with starch to form a bluish-black color. Do you observe a color change outside the bag, inside the bag, or in both places? _____

3. Use complete sentences to explain the results of the starch/iodine experiment.

Osmosis is the facilitated diffusion of *water* across a semipermeable membrane. Notice that we are now considering the movement of the *solvent*, not the solute. When solutes cannot cross a membrane, or their diffusion rate is very slow, water molecules will follow their own concentration gradient which leads them to the solution with the greater solute concentration. Thus, osmosis results in the movement of water from areas of lower solute concentration to areas of higher solute concentration (Fig. 7.5).

Osmosis is a form of passive transport; no energy is required since the water is moving down its concentration gradient. However, because water is polar, living cells use transport proteins called *aquaporins* to allow the polar water molecules to cross easily via facilitated diffusion.

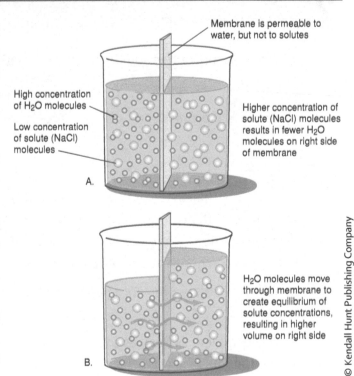

Membrane is permeable to water, but not to solutes

High concentration of H$_2$O molecules

Low concentration of solute (NaCl) molecules

Higher concentration of solute (NaCl) molecules results in fewer H$_2$O molecules on right side of membrane

A.

H$_2$O molecules move through membrane to create equilibrium of solute concentrations, resulting in higher volume on right side

B.

© Kendall Hunt Publishing Company

Figure 7.5   Osmosis. A) The two solutions are separated by a membrane that is only permeable to water. B) Water moves passively to the solution with higher solute concentration.

CONSIDER FURTHER

?

We have seen how polarity, charge, and size can affect the ability of molecules to diffuse. Other factors that affect the diffusion rate of molecules are temperature and the size of the concentration gradient.

1. Explain why an increase in temperature would increase the rate of diffusion. *Hint: Look back at Fig. 7.1.*

2. Do you think the rate of diffusion would be faster between two solutions that have more similar solute concentrations, or between two solutions that differ greatly (i.e., a *steeper* concentration gradient)? Explain your reasoning.

The **tonicity** of a solution describes its relative concentration of solutes as compared to another solution. The tonicity of a solution directly affects water movement across the semipermeable membrane, which is extremely important in biological systems since all cells require water in the correct amounts. A cell will not survive if either too much water enters or exits.

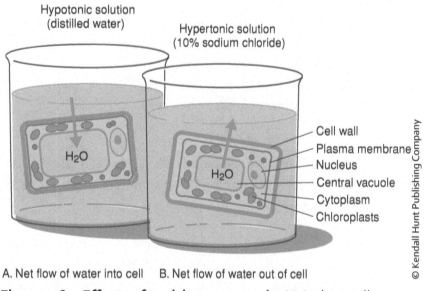

A. Net flow of water into cell   B. Net flow of water out of cell

Figure 7.6   Effects of tonicity on osmosis. A) A plant cell surrounded by a hypotonic solution will gain water in its vacuole. B) A plant cell surrounded by a hypertonic solution will lose water from its vacuole.

Consider the solution that surrounds a cell. A **hypertonic** solution has a higher concentration of solutes than the cell. Water will leave the cell as it moves toward the more concentrated side. A **hypotonic** solution has a lower concentration of solutes than the cell. In this case, water will enter the cell (because the solution inside the cell is hypertonic). Fig. 7.6 shows the effects of hypertonic and hypotonic solutions on a plant cell. An **isotonic** solution has an equal solute concentration as that of the cell. As a result, there is no net water movement (i.e., no gain or loss) across the membrane.

Observe Plasmolysis in Plant Cells

Exercise 4

Plasmolysis is the shrinking of plant cells within their cell walls resulting from a loss of water from their vacuoles. You will use a sodium chloride (NaCl) solution to observe plasmolysis in living cells of *Elodea*.

Procedure:

1. Obtain a single *Elodea* leaf and prepare a wet mount on a glass slide. Examine the cells under high magnification using a compound microscope.
2. Add a drop of 30% NaCl to the edge of the coverslip and draw the solution across the leaf by touching a piece of tissue or paper towel to the opposite edge of the coverslip.
3. Allow 1–2 minutes for the cells to acclimate to the surrounding solution. Examine the cells under high magnification again.

INTERPRET THE RESULTS

1. Do the *Elodea* cells appear to have lost water, gained water, or was there no change?

2. Based on your findings, was the 30% NaCl solution hypertonic, hypotonic, or isotonic to the cytoplasm within *Elodea* cells?

3. Animal cells like red blood cells will burst if allowed to remain in a hypotonic solution, but plant cells will not burst. How can you explain this? What difference between these two cells is responsible?

4. A patient that requires intravenous fluids to increase blood volume will receive normal saline solution, which is a 0.9% NaCl solution. Do you think normal saline solution is hypertonic, hypotonic, or isotonic to the solute concentration of blood? Explain your choice by considering the different outcomes.

Experiment: Osmotic Effects of Solutions that Differ in Tonicity

Exercise 5

Your group will be asked by your instructor to complete some or all the following challenges. You will again use dialysis tubing to create artificial cells as you did before; however, this time you must completely seal both ends of each cell because you will be frequently weighing the cell to track the gain or loss of water.

General Procedure:

1. Decide which solutions you will use for **all** your experimental challenges and check with your instructor before you begin them all at the same time.

2. Fill a beaker with 150 mL of sucrose solution. There are three different solutions of sucrose: 1%, 10%, and 20%. The solution you choose will depend on the challenge you are trying to complete. Sucrose is a disaccharide that is too large to pass through the membrane. *You will not use tap water for any solutions during this experiment.*

3. Tie one end of a piece of dialysis tubing and fill the bag with 10 mL of your choice of sucrose solution, depending on the challenge. Use great accuracy when using the graduated cylinder to measure exactly 10 mL of solution and take care not to spill any solution when pouring into your bag. Tightly seal the other end of the bag, leaving a little airspace in case of expansion.

4. Dry off the "cell" and weigh it to the nearest 0.1 gram, this is the initial weight. Submerge the cell in the beaker and start a timer.
5. Remove the cell, pat it dry, and weigh it every 10 minutes for 40 minutes. Record your data in the appropriate table for each challenge.

Challenge #1: Cause the cell to lose water.

1. For the cell to lose water, must the surrounding solution be hypertonic, hypotonic, or isotonic? _____
2. Which solution will you choose for the beaker?   **1%   10%   20%**
3. Which solution will you choose for the "cell"?   **1%   10%   20%**
4. Conduct your experiment and enter the data in the table below.

Initial weight (g)	Weight at 10 min (g)	Weight at 20 min (g)	Weight at 30 min (g)	Weight at 40 min (g)

5. Add your data to the class data.

Challenge #2: Do not allow the cell to gain or lose water.

1. For the cell to remain the same weight over the course of the experiment, must the surrounding solution be hypertonic, hypotonic, or isotonic? _____
2. Which solution will you choose for the beaker?   **1%   10%   20%**
3. Which solution will you choose for the "cell"?   **1%   10%   20%**
4. Conduct your experiment and enter the data in the table below.

Initial weight (g)	Weight at 10 min (g)	Weight at 20 min (g)	Weight at 30 min (g)	Weight at 40 min (g)

5. Add your data to the class data.

Challenge #3: Cause the cell to gain water.

1. For the cell to gain water, must the surrounding solution be hypertonic, hypotonic, or isotonic? _____

2. Which solution will you choose for the beaker?   **1%   10%   20%**

3. Which solution will you choose for the "cell"?   **1%   10%   20%**

4. Conduct your experiment and enter the data in the table below.

Initial weight (g)	Weight at 10 min (g)	Weight at 20 min (g)	Weight at 30 min (g)	Weight at 40 min (g)

5. Add your data to the class data.

Challenge #4: Two-cell experiment: Cause both cells to gain water, but one more than the other.

1. For both cells to gain water, must the surrounding solutions be hypertonic, hypotonic, or isotonic? _____

2. Choose one solution to use in both beakers: **1%   10%   20%**

3. Which solution will you choose for cell A?   **1%   10%   20%**

4. Which solution will you choose for cell B?   **1%   10%   20%**

5. Conduct both experiments simultaneously and enter the data in the table below.

	Initial weight (g)	Weight at 10 min (g)	Weight at 20 min (g)	Weight at 30 min (g)	Weight at 40 min (g)
Cell A					
Cell B					

6. Add your data to the class data.

GRAPHICAL ANALYSIS

Use the class data to create a single graph that shows mass (g) vs time (min) for each of the four "cells". Label the lines 1, 2, 3, 4a, and 4b according to the challenge each line represents.

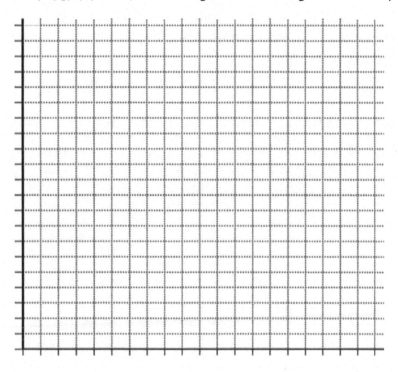

Did you complete the challenges successfully? _____

Do your data look different from what you expected? Are there any inconsistencies? _____

_____

How about the overall class data, were the results as expected? Explain why or why not. _____

_____

_____

TEST YOUR UNDERSTANDING

1. Which statement most accurately describes Brownian motion?

   a. It is the random vibration of individual atoms caused by fast-moving electrons.
   b. It is the random movement of small particles in solution caused by collisions with fast-moving molecules.
   c. It is the random movement of water molecules caused by collisions with each other.
   d. It is the directional movement of solutes down their concentration gradient.

2. Your blood plasma is mostly *water*, but it carries many dissolved substances like *oxygen gas*, *hormones*, and *glucose* monomers. Identify each of the substances written in italics as either the **solute** or the **solvent** in the plasma solution.

3. Consider two solutions separated by a semipermeable membrane. One solution is pure water while the other has a 10% glucose concentration. Glucose is allowed to diffuse down its concentration gradient.

   a. What will be the O_2 concentration of both solutions when equilibrium is reached?
   b. If a living cell wanted to bring in greater amounts of solute than it has at equilibrium, what would be required?

4. Osmosis is _____.

   a. the simple diffusion of large ionic compounds through a semipermeable membrane
   b. the diffusion of large, charged molecules through a transport protein
   c. the active (energy-requiring) transport of water
   d. the movement of water through a semipermeable membrane

5. *THINK FURTHER:* Dialysis tubing is like the nephrons of our kidneys. Nephrons carry filtrate from the blood through the specialized environment of the kidney, which creates urine by absorbing nutrients, salts, and water from the filtrate as the waste is concentrated. The kidney plays a large role in maintaining proper levels of hydration in the body; if you were to examine the kidney you would find extremely high NaCl concentrations within the tissues surrounding the nephron. Why do the tissues of the kidney maintain such high salt concentrations? State the tonicities of the tissue fluid and the filtrate to support your explanation.

CHAPTER 8
THE CARDIOVASCULAR SYSTEM

 Laboratory Objectives

By the end of this laboratory, the student should be able to:

- trace the path of blood through the heart: name the chambers and valves through which the blood passes and identify blood as either oxygen-rich or oxygen-poor at each location;
- understand the electrocardiogram (ECG), locate a pulse, measure heart rate, and calculate recovery time after exercise;
- describe the double circulation of blood through pulmonary and systemic circuits;
- recognize the structural differences between arteries and veins, and how these differences relate to blood pressure before and after crossing a capillary bed;
- identify red blood cells, white blood cells, and platelets under a microscope, and describe the important structural and functional characteristics of the formed elements.

The heart is a muscular pump within most animals that circulates blood through the many **blood vessels** in our body. **Blood** nourishes our body's cells with nutrients (**glucose, amino acids,** etc.), **oxygen gas (O_2), hormones, salts,** and **vitamins** and removes wastes such as **carbon dioxide gas (CO_2).** Blood also serves our immune system by circulating white blood cells that attack foreign invaders like bacteria and viruses.

In this lab exercise, you will observe a heart model and a dissected sheep heart to learn the major anatomical features of the heart. You will also learn how the electrocardiogram reflects heart function, how to locate your pulse and measure your heart rate, and observe the structure of arteries, veins, and the formed elements of the blood under a microscope.

Exercise 1

Use the labeled diagrams of the external anatomy (Fig. 8.1) and internal anatomy (Fig. 8.2) of the heart to *locate these structures on the heart model* on display in the laboratory. Your instructor will indicate which structures are most important for your learning goals.

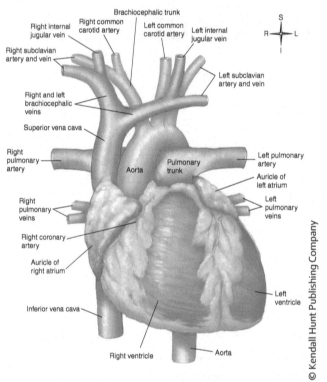

© Kendall Hunt Publishing Company

Figure 8.1   External anatomy of the human heart.

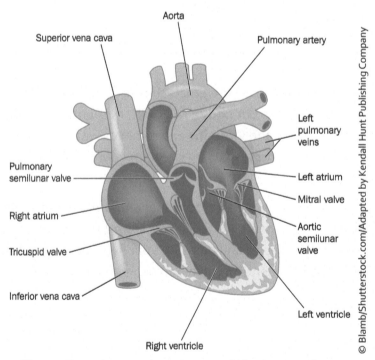

© Blamb/Shutterstock.com/Adapted by Kendall Hunt Publishing Company

Figure 8.2   Internal anatomy of the human heart.

TRACE THE PATH OF BLOOD

?

1. Blood returns from the body to the heart via the **superior vena cava** and **inferior vena cava**.

Which <u>chamber</u> of the heart receives this blood? _____

Is this blood oxygen-rich or oxygen-poor? _____

2. The blood then passes through the **tricuspid valve** to enter the **right ventricle**.

Which <u>valve</u> opens to allow blood to exit the right ventricle? _____

_____ To which organ(s) will this blood travel? _____

3. Blood returns from the lungs to the heart via the **pulmonary veins**.

Which <u>chamber</u> of the heart receives this blood?_____

Is this blood oxygen-rich or oxygen-poor? _____

4. The blood then passes through the **bicuspid valve** to enter the **left ventricle**.

Which <u>valve</u> opens to allow blood to exit the left ventricle? _____

_____

5. Blood leaving the left side of the heart will next enter the _____,
a large artery that delivers oxygen-rich blood to the body.

Exercise 2

Examine the dissected sheep heart on display in the laboratory. Locate the structures you studied in Exercise 1 and *label as many of these structures as you can* on Figure 8.3.

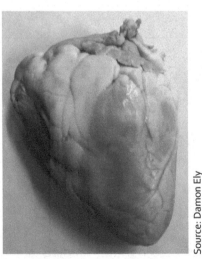 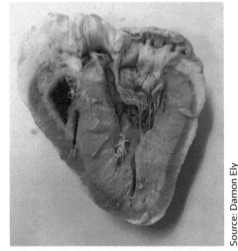

Source: Damon Ely

Source: Damon Ely

Figure 8.3   Dissected sheep heart. Ventral view of external (*left*)
and internal (*right*) anatomy.

The alternate contraction (**systole**) and relaxation (**diastole**) of the ventricles creates pressure waves of blood known as **pulses** that stretch the arteries and can be detected in various places on the body. Your **heart rate** can be determined by measuring the frequency of the pulse; typical resting heart rates are between 65 and 80 beats per minute (bpm), but may be as low as 40 bpm in some athletes.

Exercise 3

Measure Your Heart Rate

1. Locate your pulse in your radial artery by lightly pressing your second and third finger to the thumb side of your inner wrist. Count the number of pulses you feel in 15 sec: _____

2. Multiply this number by 4 to calculate your resting heart rate (**HR**) in beats per minute:

_____ beats in 15 sec × 4 = _____ bpm

3. Repeat this procedure a few times until you can easily measure your HR. Next, we will do an investigation that will require you to be able to find the pulse quickly.

INVESTIGATION: FACTORS AFFECTING CARDIOVASCULAR HEALTH IN WOMEN VS. MEN

Observation: Medical research has shown that women have lower cardiovascular health risk and live longer than men. Typically, healthy individuals (like trained athletes) have a lower resting HR and, after vigorous exercise, their HR more quickly returns to the resting rate (known as *recovery time*).

Question: Could the differences in heart health and longevity between women and men be explained by these variables (resting HR and recovery time)?

Write a *Hypothesis*:

_____

_____

Procedure:

WARNING: Do not do the following exercises if you have heart or lung problems.

1. Measure your resting HR as you did before. ***Resting HR = _____ bpm***
2. Exercise vigorously for 3 minutes by jogging in place or doing jumping-jacks. You should really be working out!
3. Measure your HR immediately after exercising ("zero-minute" reading) and at 1-min intervals for the first 4 minutes. Record your data in Table 8.1. Thereafter, measure your HR every 2 minutes until it returns to the resting rate.

Table 8.1   Heart rate (HR) following vigorous exercise

Time (minutes)	HR (bpm)	Time (minutes)	HR (bpm)	Time (minutes)	HR (bpm)
0		6		16	
1		8		18	
2		10		20	
3		12		22	
4		14		24	

4. How many minutes passed until your HR returned to normal? _____ min
   This is your **recovery time (RT)**.

5. Add your resting HR and recovery time to the class data (see your instructor) and enter the class data in Table 8.2.

Table 8.2   Resting heart rate (HR) and recovery times of female (F) and male (M) students

F/M	Resting HR (bpm)	RT (min)	F/M	Resting HR (bpm)	RT (min)	F/M	Resting HR (bpm)	RT (min)	F/M	Resting HR (bpm)	RT (min)

6. Calculate the average RT for the female students and then again for the male students.

   Average Resting HR for Females: _____ bpm   Average Recovery Time for Females: _____ min

   Average Resting HR for Males: _____ bpm   Average Recovery Time for Males: _____ min

7. Create bar graphs of these data using the blank graphs below.

Resting Heart Rate in Females vs. Males

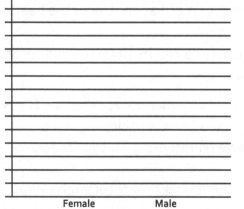

Female   Male

Recovery Time in Females vs. Males

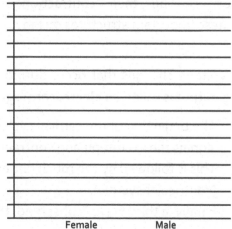

Female   Male

- Does the evidence support or reject your hypothesis? Explain

  _____

  _____

  _____

- Review Table 8.2. Compare the number of female and male students and the amount of variation among the data. Are there reasons you might hesitate to draw firm conclusions based on your data? Explain

  _____

  _____

  _____

CONTROL OF THE HEARTBEAT

The cardiac cycle is the series of events that occur in the heart from one heartbeat to the next. The initiation of the heartbeat occurs in the pacemaker region of the right atrium known as the **sinoatrial (SA) node**. The SA node causes the atria to contract by sending an impulse every 0.85 seconds that sweeps through the cardiac muscle cells of the heart. This impulse reaches the **atrioventricular (AV) node** and then continues through **Purkinje fibers** that line the walls of the ventricles, causing their contraction. Locate these important structures on Fig. 8.4.

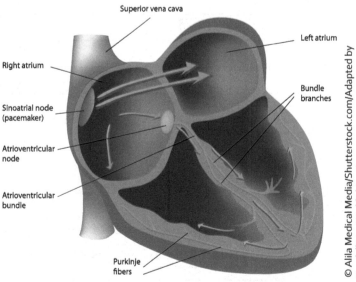

Figure 8.4   Cardiac control of the heartbeat.

© Alila Medical Media/Shutterstock.com/Adapted by Kendall Hunt Publishing Company

The voltage changes that occur during the cardiac cycle can be detected and recorded; the resulting output is called an **electrocardiogram (ECG)**.

- The beginning of the cardiac cycle is marked by a smaller wave, called the **P wave**, that signals the excitation and contraction of the atria (atrial systole).
- This is followed by the much larger **QRS wave** representing ventricular contraction (ventricular systole).
- Finally, a third wave is observed, the **T wave**, that marks ventricular relaxation (ventricular diastole).

Use Fig. 8.5 to understand how these regions of the ECG are related to the events in the heart.

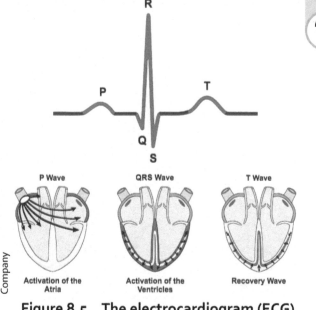

Figure 8.5   The electrocardiogram (ECG) and related events of the cardiac cycle.

UNDERSTANDING THE ECG

?

1. Why might you expect the QRS wave to be greater in magnitude than the P wave?

_____

_____

2. During which portion of the ECG would the atrioventricular valves forcefully close?

_____

3. During which portion of the ECG would the semilunar valves forcefully close?

_____

4. Within your group, explain what causes the *lub-dub* sound of the heartbeat.

8.3 DOUBLE CIRCULATION

When a unit of blood crosses over a capillary bed, the pressure pushing it along drops considerably. After blood crosses the capillary beds of the lungs, it first returns to the heart before circulating through the body. After blood crosses the capillary beds of the body, it returns to the heart before circulating through the lungs. In this way, the circulatory pattern of blood flow is described as **double circulation**, where blood flows through two circuits: the **pulmonary circuit** (through the lungs) and the **systemic circuit** (through the body proper). By returning blood to the heart directly after crossing a capillary bed, blood pressure is restored to move blood more efficiently through the next circuit.

The **pulmonary circuit** follows blood leaving the right side of the heart, crossing the lungs, and returning via the pulmonary veins. The **systemic circuit** follows blood leaving the left side of the heart and passing through all of the body *except* the lungs before returning to the heart in the vena cavae.

Exercise 4 Use colored pencils to represent the oxygen status of the blood as it passes through the heart and pulmonary and systemic circuits by *coloring in the heart chambers, heart vessels, and capillary beds* in Fig. 8.6. Use red to represent blood that is oxygen-rich, and blue to represent blood that is oxygen-poor.

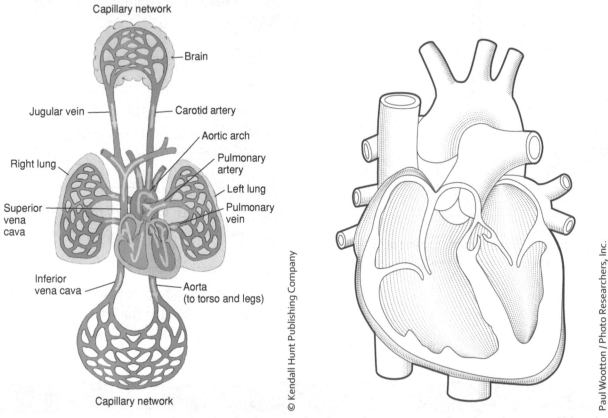

Figure 8.6 **Double circulation in the human body.** Left: Conceptualized pathways of blood through both systemic and pulmonary circuits. Right: Internal anatomy of the heart.

8.4 BLOOD VESSELS: ARTERIES, VEINS, AND CAPILLARY BEDS

Blood travels through the body within blood vessels of three types: arteries, veins, and capillaries.

- **Arteries** carry blood away from the heart (you can remember *arteries/away*) under high pressure due to the forceful contraction of the ventricles.
- Blood then travels across extremely thin-walled (only a single cell layer) **capillary beds** where oxygen gas, carbon dioxide, nutrients, and other dissolved solutes exchange with the tissue fluids surrounding the body's cells. Due to the collective increase in cross-sectional area, blood pressure drops considerably over a capillary bed.
- **Veins** return low-pressure blood back into the heart (you can remember *veins/into*) after blood crosses a capillary bed.

ARTERIES VS. VEINS

Because blood pressure differs greatly between arteries (high BP) and veins (low BP), their physical structure differs as well.

As shown in Fig. 8.7:

- the layer of smooth muscle cells in arteries is thicker than in veins,
- arteries have a smaller cross-sectional area through which blood flows, and
- many veins have valves inside which are not found in arteries.

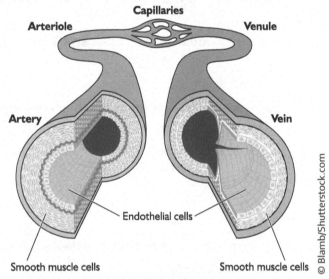

Figure 8.7   Anatomy of blood vessels.

© Blamb/Shutterstock.com

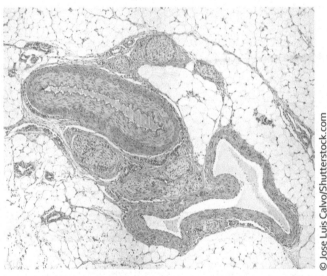

© Jose Luis Calvo/Shutterstock.com

Figure 8.8   Photomicrograph of blood vessels.

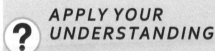

⟨?⟩ APPLY YOUR UNDERSTANDING

1. Determine which vessel in Fig. 8.8 is the artery and which is the vein. Label both on the figure.

2. Determine which cell layer of these vessels is the smooth muscle. Label them on the figure.

Exercise 5

Using a microscope, examine a prepared slide showing an artery and a vein in cross-section. In the space below, make a sketch of the artery and vein as you see them under the microscope. Label both types of vessels and note their characteristics.

STRUCTURE AND FUNCTION OF BLOOD VESSELS

1. What would happen to an artery if it had a muscle layer similar in structure to a vein?

2. Consider that some of the blood entering the aorta must travel as far as the foot to deliver oxygen gas and nutrients to those cells. How does the smaller cross-sectional area of arteries help in the delivery of this blood?

3. Why are valves necessary in veins but not in arteries? What might happen if veins did not have valves?

4. Do materials like oxygen gas and nutrients exchange between blood and tissues while blood is traveling through arteries and veins? Why or why not?

8.5 THE FORMED ELEMENTS: BLOOD CELLS AND PLATELETS

Blood is a type of connective tissue that appears simply as a thick liquid. In fact, blood has two major components: a liquid portion known as **plasma**, and a cellular component known as the **formed elements**. Plasma consists mostly of water with dissolved solutes such as ions, nutrients, and large circulating proteins. The formed elements are the red blood cells (**erythrocytes**), white blood cells (**leukocytes**), and platelets (**thrombocytes**).

Erythrocytes—Red blood cells

Red blood cells are the most numerous cell in the blood. The erythrocytes are smaller than white blood cells and have a biconcave (pinched at the middle) shape, giving them a light spot at their center when viewed under a

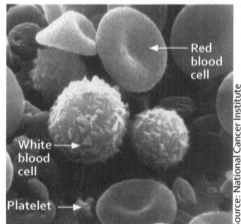

Figure 8.9   Electron micrograph of the formed elements.

microscope. Red blood cells lack a nucleus, allowing them to be packed with **hemoglobin,** a protein that carries oxygen gas. Hemoglobin is found in all vertebrates and even in many invertebrates.

Leukocytes—White blood cells

White blood cells defend against invading microorganisms and other foreign substances as part of our immune system. White blood cells occur less frequently than erythrocytes and they are not confined to the blood—leukocytes can leave capillaries and enter the surrounding tissue fluid. Leukocytes are larger than erythrocytes and have a visible nucleus making them rounded (see Fig. 8.9).

Thrombocytes—Platelets

Platelets are tiny fragments of cells formed in the bone marrow. Platelets are a primary factor in the process of forming a blood clot when a vessel is injured. Under the microscope platelets are small, round dots.

Exercise 6

Using a microscope, observe a slide of a human blood smear and compare it to Fig. 8.10. Identify the different formed elements by looking for the characteristics described above.

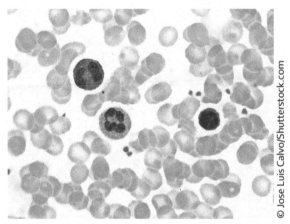

© Jose Luis Calvo/Shutterstock.com

Figure 8.10   Human blood smear.

APPLY YOUR UNDERSTANDING

?

1. Label each of the three formed elements on Fig. 8.10.

2. Make a brief list of the important structural and functional characteristics for each formed element:

Erythrocytes: Function(s)_____

Structural characteristics: _____

Leukocytes: Function(s)_____

Structural characteristics: _____

Platelets: Function(s)_____

Structural characteristics: _____

CHAPTER 9
THE RESPIRATORY SYSTEM

 Laboratory Objectives

By the end of this laboratory, the student should be able to:

- locate and identify the major structures of the human respiratory system;
- explain how the physical characteristics of the nasal cavity, larynx, and trachea relate to the functional roles of these structures;
- describe the exchange of gases across the alveoli and explain the ways in which the structure of the alveoli increases the efficiency of this process;
- understand negative-pressure breathing using the diaphragm and rib muscles.

The lungs are sites of gas exchange between your body and the air around you. The atmosphere contains approximately 21% oxygen gas (O_2), which diffuses across the thin, moistened internal surfaces of your lungs to enter your bloodstream. At the same time, the higher concentration of carbon dioxide (CO_2) in the blood causes CO_2 to diffuse out of the blood to the air spaces of the lungs to be exhaled. In this way, vital O_2 needed for cellular respiration in the mitochondria of our cells, and the CO_2 waste created by this same process, are exchanged with every inhale and exhale.

Our respiratory system performs other functions too. The circulation of CO_2 in the form of bicarbonate ion (HCO_3^-) serves as an important buffer system to any changes in blood pH. Likewise, our breathing rate can adjust to control the release of CO_2 to maintain homeostasis of blood pH at 7.4. In addition to maintaining blood pH, our respiratory system also contains our voice box, where the vocal folds vibrate to produce the sounds with which we communicate.

In this lab exercise, you will become familiar with the major organs in the human respiratory system by observing models and analyzing tissues under the microscope.

Exercise 1

Use Fig. 9.1 to *locate these structures on the models* on display in the laboratory.

THE NASAL CAVITY

The nostrils contain hairs that collect large airborne particles like dust and dirt, preventing them from entering the lungs. The nostrils are the openings of the **nasal cavity**, a series of narrow passages lined with **mucous membranes**.

Mucous membranes consist of **ciliated epithelial cells** and cells that create a layer of sticky mucus to trap finer particles (like bacteria and other microbes) that are moved upward and out via the pulsating action of the fine cilia. The passage of air over these surfaces also serves to *warm* and *humidify* the air before reaching the lungs.

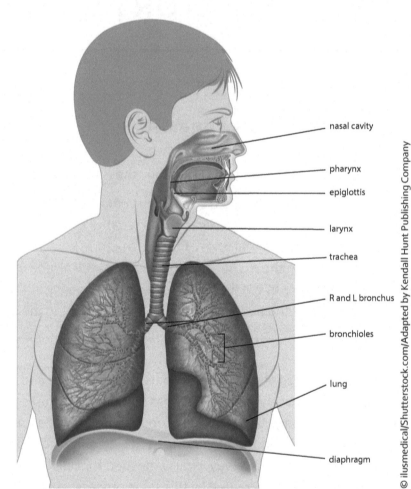

Figure 9.1   Organs of the Respiratory System.

© ilusmedical/Shutterstock.com/Adapted by Kendall Hunt Publishing Company

CONSIDER FURTHER . . .

1. Why is it beneficial to warm the air before it enters your lungs? Which organ might be the most important to consider if the air brought into your lungs is not warmed?

2. Why are respiratory surfaces typically <u>thin</u> and <u>moist</u>? How do each of these traits promote efficient diffusion?

THE LARYNX

The larynx is a large box-like structure in the neck that houses the vocal folds (aka vocal cords) and passes inhaled air to the trachea and lungs (Fig. 9.2). The horseshoe-shaped **hyoid bone** provides an attachment point for muscles that raise the larynx during swallowing. This action pushes the larynx up against the **epiglottis**, a flap of elastic cartilage that prevents food from entering the airways during swallowing.

The larynx has an anterior covering of **thyroid cartilage** consisting of two halves that meet at an acute angle we commonly refer to as the Adam's apple. The thyroid cartilage provides protection and housing for the **vocal folds**; this area is known as the voice box.

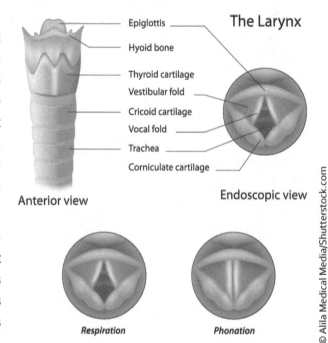

Figure 9.2 Structure of the larynx.

THE LOWER RESPIRATORY TRACT

The lower respiratory tract begins with the **trachea**, a long tube descending from the larynx that is composed of repeated rings of hyaline **cartilage** that maintain an open passage for air flow. Ciliated epithelial cells line the inner surfaces of the trachea, which eventually splits into the right and left **bronchi** (singular: *bronchus*) to deliver air into the **lungs**.

The bronchi divide repeatedly into smaller **bronchioles** that branch extensively throughout the lungs. Each bronchiole terminates in **alveoli**, tiny sacs of air (Fig. 9.3) that exchange gases with the blood.

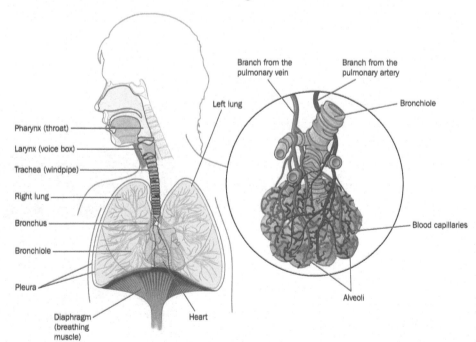

Figure 9.3 Human respiratory system showing the organization of the alveoli.

Exercise 2

The structural role of the cartilage holding open the trachea is easily seen under the microscope, especially when the trachea is compared to the esophagus (which is posterior to the trachea). Ciliated epithelial cells can be easily observed by looking at the trachea through the microscope.

A. Under low power, observe the slide showing a cross-section of the trachea and esophagus. Compare what you observe to Fig. 9.4. Label the <u>esophagus</u>, <u>trachea</u>, and <u>tracheal cartilage</u> on Fig. 9.4.

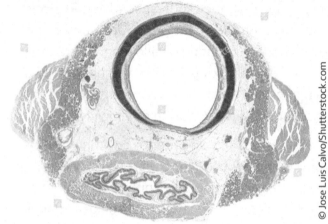

Figure 9.4   Cross-section of trachea and esophagus.

CONSIDER FURTHER . . .

The esophagus contracts its smooth muscle layer to move food to the stomach (a phenomenon called *peristalsis*).

How does this fact help explain why the esophagus appears differently from the trachea in Fig. 9.4?

B. Position the slide so that a section of the internal surface layer of the trachea is at the center, then increase the magnification until you can clearly see the ciliated epithelial cells covered with a layer of mucus and resting on the connective tissue below them. Compare what you see to Fig. 9.5. Label the <u>mucus</u>, <u>cilia</u>, <u>epithelial cell</u>, and <u>connective tissue</u> on Fig. 9.5.

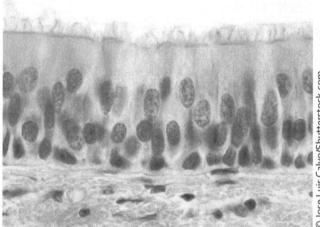

Figure 9.5   Ciliated epithelial cells of the trachea.

The capillary beds that lie in the interstitial spaces between alveoli carry O_2-poor/CO_2-rich blood that has returned from the rest of the body and then pumped by the heart into the pulmonary arteries.

As the blood travels over the thin-walled alveoli, which are filled with inhaled air (O_2-rich/CO_2-poor), oxygen gas and carbon dioxide move passively via simple diffusion down their respective concentration gradients as shown in Fig. 9.6.

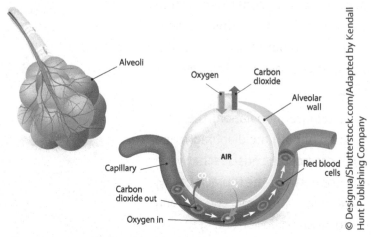

Oxygen • Carbon dioxide • Alveoli • Alveolar wall • Capillary • AIR • Red blood cells • Carbon dioxide out • CO₂ • O₂ • Oxygen in

Figure 9.6   Gas exchange between a blood capillary and an alveolus.

Observe a prepared slide of human lung tissue that has been stained dark purple. Make a sketch of what you see in the box on the right and label the multiple alveoli.

Exercise 3

APPLY YOUR UNDERSTANDING

Fig. 9.7 shows a section of a lung with emphysema, a disease caused mostly by smoking that breaks down alveolar walls.

1. Describe *how* the emphysematous lung tissue appears differently from your drawing of healthy lung tissue.

_____

_____

2. Explain how the altered structure of the lung tissue leads to difficulty with breathing in individuals suffering from emphysema.

_____

_____

_____

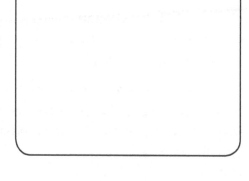

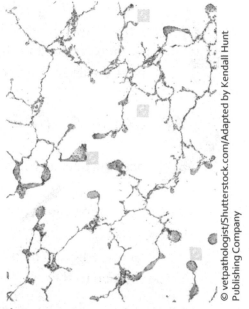

Figure 9.7   Lung tissue with emphysema.

The lungs are contained within our thoracic cavity, which is separated from our abdominal cavity by a large sheet-like muscle, the **diaphragm**.

During an inhalation, the contraction of both the diaphragm and the **intercostal muscles** between the ribs enlarges the thoracic cavity, increasing its volume and causing air to be drawn inside (Fig. 9.8). This happens because the diaphragm is pulled downward and the rib cage spreads outward.

During an exhalation, the diaphragm and intercostals relax, reducing the volume of the thoracic cavity and expelling air.

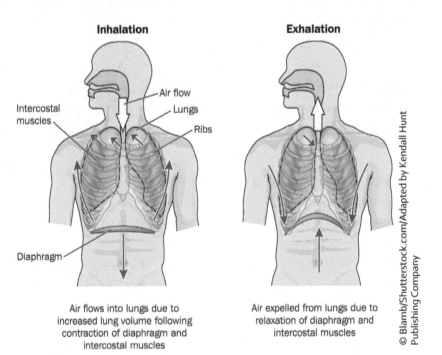

Air flows into lungs due to increased lung volume following contraction of diaphragm and intercostal muscles

Air expelled from lungs due to relaxation of diaphragm and intercostal muscles

© Blamb/Shutterstock.com/Adapted by Kendall Hunt Publishing Company

Figure 9.8   Negative-pressure breathing.

Because these muscular actions reduce air pressure in the body cavity that air must rush in to fill, this type of breathing is known as **negative-pressure breathing**. Contrast this with animals like frogs who must fill their lungs by physically pushing air (positive pressure) through the glottis and into the trachea.

Exercise 4

Examine the lung simulator on display. The simulator consists of a large dome (the thoracic cavity), balloons (lungs) connected to the outside air by tubes through a stopper (airways), and a rubber sheet (the diaphragm). Observe the "lungs" as you gently move the lever up and down.

APPLY YOUR UNDERSTANDING

1. In what direction did you move the lever (i.e., the diaphragm) to cause the lungs to fill?

2. Does this represent a contraction or a relaxation of the diaphragm?

3. A traumatic injury could result in a collapsed lung. In this case, what would directly cause the lung to collapse?

4. Could a collapsed lung continue to function? Why or why not?

CHAPTER 10
THE DIGESTIVE SYSTEM

 Laboratory Objectives

By the end of this laboratory, the student should be able to:

- list the major organs of the digestive system and identify their general functions;
- describe how the structural characteristics of a given digestive organ are related to the efficient functioning of that organ;
- recognize the structural features of the tissues and organs observed using the microscope;
- identify the substances produced by various organs of the alimentary canal and the accessory organs, and describe how these substances contribute to each organ's function.

The stomach might be the first organ that comes to your mind when you think of the digestive system. However, the digestive system is composed of many connected organs, each carrying out very specific functions, that span a considerable length of most animals' bodies. The primary purpose of the digestive system is to process ingested food to supply the body with the organic nutrients (e.g., glucose, amino acids), vitamins, minerals, ions, and the water it needs to function properly.

Food processing in animals occurs in four stages: ingestion, digestion, absorption, and elimination. **Ingestion** is the initial acquisition of food through the mouth. **Digestion** refers to the breaking down of food materials using muscles, acids, and enzymes. **Absorption** of monomers and other small substances involves the transport of these materials across cell membranes and entrance into the blood. **Elimination** removes undigested materials through the anus in animals with complete digestive systems.

In this lab exercise, you will examine the various organs of the digestive system using diagrams, models, and observations of tissues under the microscope. Be sure to pay close attention to how the structural features of these organs are suited to their different functions.

Exercise 1

Use the labeled diagram of the human digestive system (Fig. 10.1) and Table 10.1 to familiarize yourself with the major digestive organs and their primary functions. *You should be able to recognize these structures on the digestive system models that are on display in the lab.*

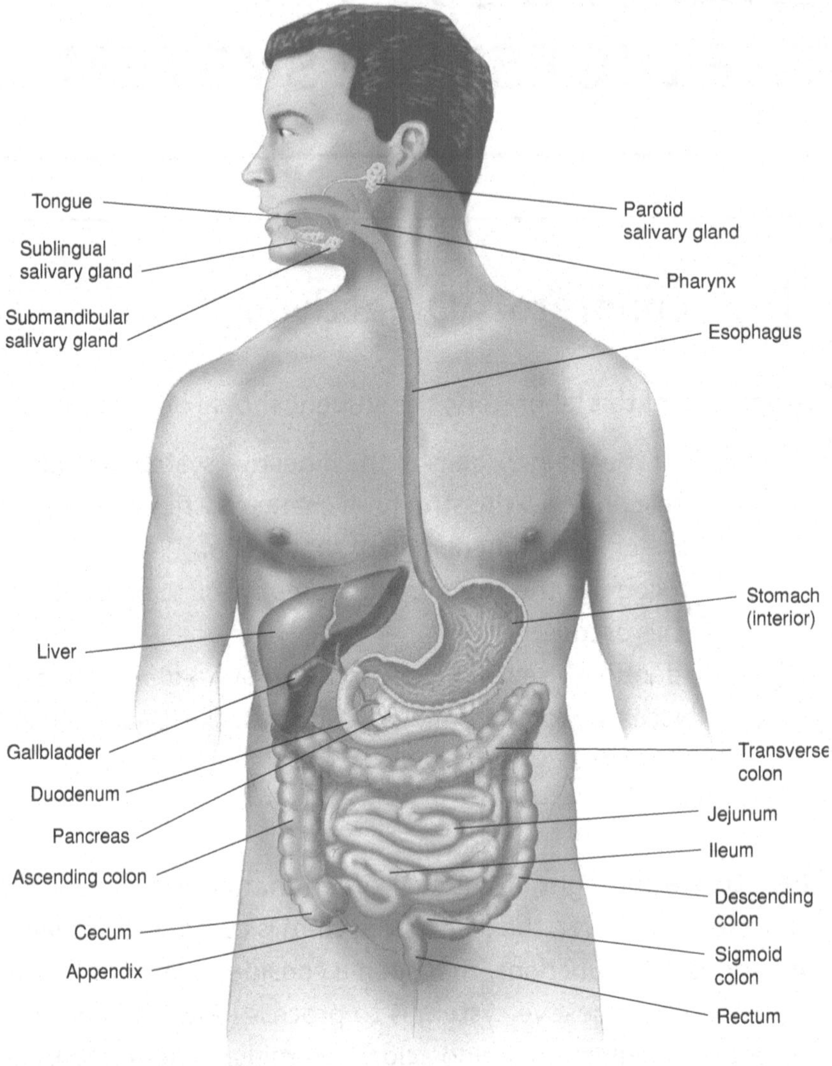

Tongue
Sublingual salivary gland
Submandibular salivary gland
Parotid salivary gland
Pharynx
Esophagus
Stomach (interior)
Liver
Gallbladder
Duodenum
Pancreas
Ascending colon
Cecum
Appendix
Transverse colon
Jejunum
Ileum
Descending colon
Sigmoid colon
Rectum

© Kendall Hunt Publishing Company

Figure 10.1 The human digestive system.

Table 10.1 Primary functions of the major digestive organs.

Structure	Primary Function
Oral cavity	Mastication (chewing) and swallowing food; starch hydrolysis
Esophagus	Carries food bolus to stomach via peristalsis
Stomach	Secretion of gastric juices that mix with food to form chyme; protein digestion
Small intestine	Combines chyme with secretions from accessory organs to complete digestion and absorption
Large intestine	Water absorption and bacterial decomposition to form feces for elimination through the anus

THE ORAL CAVITY

The oral cavity is responsible for both mechanical and chemical digestion. **Mechanical digestion** refers to the fragmentation of food materials due to physical manipulation via muscular contraction and abrasion/grinding against hard surfaces. **Chemical digestion** refers to the molecular alteration of food materials due to denaturation and hydrolysis via acidic compounds and digestive enzymes.

In the mouth, mechanical digestion is accomplished by the chewing action of the **jaws** and **teeth**. As you will see in other areas of the digestive system, this is a strategy to increase the surface area for further chemical digestion. The various **salivary glands** (Fig. 10.1) produce **saliva** to lubricate the ingested food for its further passage and to begin the digestion of starch due to active **salivary amylase** enzymes. Salivary amylase hydrolyzes starch polymers to produce the disaccharide maltose.

Swallowing is initiated by raising the **tongue** to the roof of the mouth and pushing the bolus of food toward the area at the back of the throat called the **pharynx**. At this point, the **soft palate** is moved upwards to prevent entry into the nasal cavity (Fig. 10.2). The raising of the larynx during swallowing acts to lower the **epiglottis** over the opening to the glottis, preventing the entry of food into the respiratory system. In this way, the bolus is directed into the esophagus as shown in Fig. 10.2.

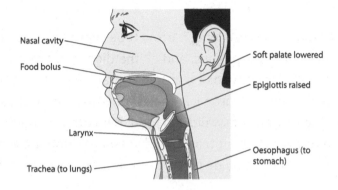

Nasal cavity
Food bolus
Larynx
Trachea (to lungs)
Soft palate lowered
Epiglottis raised
Oesophagus (to stomach)

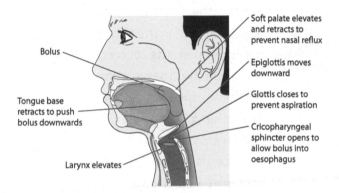

Bolus
Tongue base retracts to push bolus downwards
Larynx elevates
Soft palate elevates and retracts to prevent nasal reflux
Epiglottis moves downward
Glottis closes to prevent aspiration
Cricopharyngeal sphincter opens to allow bolus into oesophagus

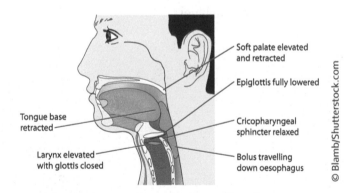

Tongue base retracted
Larynx elevated with glottis closed
Soft palate elevated and retracted
Epiglottis fully lowered
Cricopharyngeal sphincter relaxed
Bolus travelling down oesophagus

Figure 10.2   The act of swallowing.

APPLY YOUR UNDERSTANDING

1. How does the act of chewing help increase the efficiency of salivary amylase?

2. Explain why you cannot breathe in through your nose while swallowing.

THE ESOPHAGUS

The esophagus is a long, narrow tube that carries food toward the stomach (Fig. 10.1). The tissue layers of the esophagus, and all the digestive organs, begins with a layer of protective epithelial cells called the **mucosa** that is in contact with the material passing through the **lumen**—the open space inside each organ. In the esophagus, the mucosa secretes mucus and fluid into the lumen to aid the passage of swallowed food. Beneath the mucosa lies a layer of connective tissue called the **submucosa** that contains blood vessels, lymphatic vessels, and nerves. The submucosa connects the mucosa to outside layers of smooth muscle named the **muscularis**.

Exercise 2

Label the terms that appear in bold in the above paragraph in the correct places on the cross-section of the esophagus shown in Fig. 10.3. Then, view a similar cross-section of the esophagus under a microscope at high power and try to identify these same tissue layers.

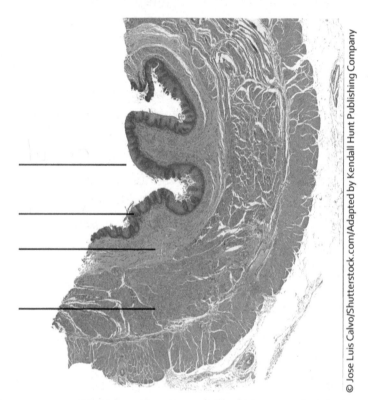

© Jose Luis Calvo/Shutterstock.com/Adapted by Kendall Hunt Publishing Company

Figure 10.3   Cross-section (partial) of the esophagus.

The downward movement of the food bolus is driven by wave-like contractions of the smooth muscle tissue in the muscularis. This movement is called **peristalsis** (Fig. 10.4) and it is the predominant mechanism pushing materials through the entire digestive system.

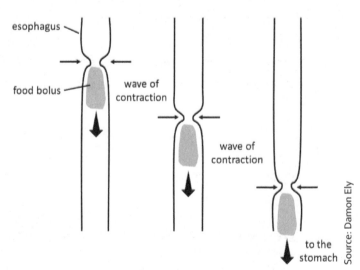

Source: Damon Ely

Figure 10.4   Peristalsis in the esophagus.

THE STOMACH

The esophagus passes through the diaphragm and upon entry into the abdominal cavity it immediately connects to the **stomach** (Fig. 10.1). The stomach is a large sac-like organ that serves to hold ingested food for further mechanical and chemical digestion. The stomach has a curved shape, with the **lesser curvature** toward the right and the **greater curvature** toward the left. Many inner folds called **rugae** are visible when the stomach is empty (Fig. 10.5). Rugae allow for the expansion of the stomach following ingestion.

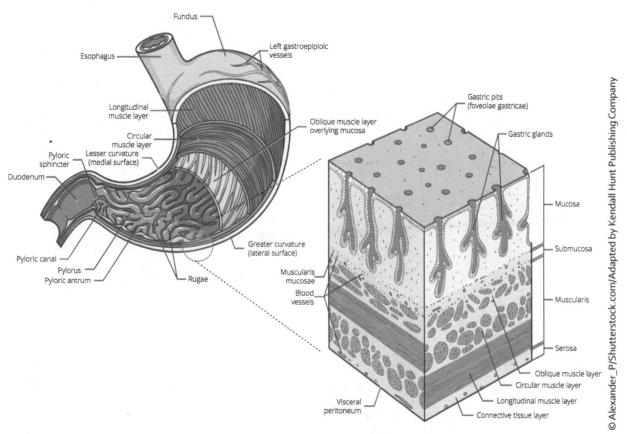

Figure 10.5   Structure of the stomach.

Digestion in the stomach is accomplished both mechanically and chemically. Unlike other parts of the digestive system, the stomach possesses three layers of muscle tissue within the muscularis: **oblique, circular,** and **longitudinal** muscles (Fig. 10.5). Each of these muscle layers contracts in a different direction to enhance the fragmentation of ingested food items.

The mucosa of the stomach contains many gastric glands containing specialized cells that produce **hydrochloric acid (HCl)** and the protein-digesting enzyme **pepsin**. These substances are components of the gastric juices, which are secreted into the lumen through large gastric pits (Fig. 10.5). The strong acid HCl gives the gastric juices an acidic pH of 1.5–3.5 that kills most microorganisms, protecting the body from potentially harmful bacteria and other microbes that may enter with food.

The low pH of the stomach also serves to denature the large, tightly-folded proteins in food, giving pepsin greater access to the peptide bonds it hydrolyzes. Unlike other enzymes of the body, pepsin can only function properly at very low pH. In these ways, HCl and pepsin work together to be an important site for protein digestion.

The resulting mixture of partially-digested food and gastric juices is called **chyme**. Chyme is allowed to leave the stomach in small amounts through the occasional opening of a muscular ring at the base of the stomach, the **pyloric sphincter** (Fig. 10.5). The pyloric sphincter acts as a valve to allow chyme to pass through to the small intestine.

THE SMALL INTESTINE

The completion of digestion and approximately 90% of nutrient absorption occurs in the **small intestine (SI)** (Fig. 10.6). The SI averages 3 m (10 ft) in length in a living person; in a cadaver, the relaxation of smooth muscle tissue doubles the length of the SI. The long length of the SI ensures that chyme will maintain contact with the inner surfaces for a longer time for complete absorption.

Three regions of the SI are recognized: the **duodenum**, the **jejunum**, and the **ileum** (Fig. 10.1). The latter two regions differ slightly in their absorptive properties; however, the duodenum is more distinct because of its connection to various *accessory organs*, which are discussed further in Section 10.2.

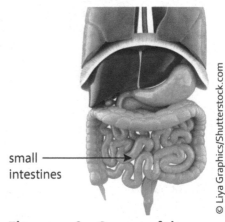

small intestines

Figure 10.6 Organs of the abdominal cavity.

In addition to the digestive enzymes it receives from the pancreas (see Section 10.2), the SI also produces its own enzymes to collectively digest carbohydrates into simple sugars, proteins into amino acids, lipids into glycerol and fatty acids, and nucleic acids into nucleotides. These monomers are then absorbed by cells that line the highly folded inner surface.

The **circular folds** of the SI (Fig. 10.7) are composed of small, finger-like **villi** that greatly increase the total surface area for absorption. The epithelial cells that line the villi have folded cell membranes called **microvilli** (Fig. 10.8) that collectively form a surface known as a **brush border** (Fig.10.9), which further increases the efficiency of absorption.

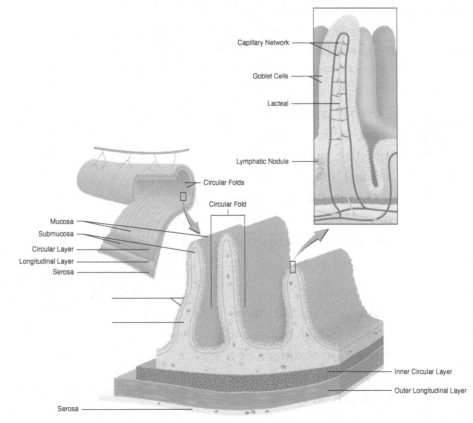

Figure 10.7 Structure of the small intestine. The inner wall consists of circular folds that increase surface area.

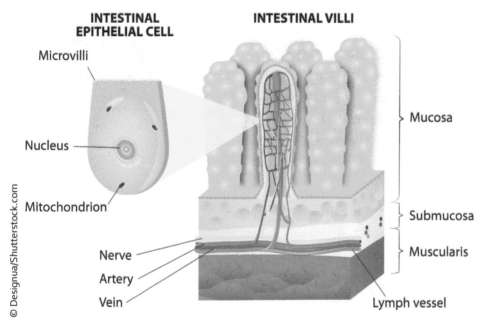

INTESTINAL EPITHELIAL CELL

Microvilli

Nucleus

Mitochondrion

INTESTINAL VILLI

Nerve

Artery

Vein

Mucosa

Submucosa

Muscularis

Lymph vessel

© Designua/Shutterstock.com

Figure 10.8 Villi and microvilli. The folded inner wall of the small intestine contains extensions of the mucosa known as villi (singular *villus*) that contain blood and lymph vessels for nutrient absorption. The exposed surface of each epithelial cell is further folded into microvilli. Villi and microvilli greatly increase the surface area of the small intestine.

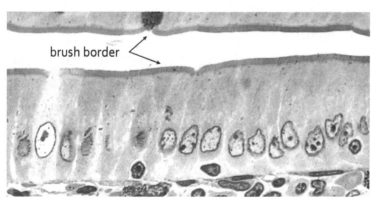

brush border

Figure 10.9 Brush border of the small intestine. The exposed surfaces (i.e., apical surfaces) of the epithelial cells lining the villi are folded into microvilli to form the brush border.

© Jose Luis Calvo/Shutterstock.com/Adapted by Kendall Hunt Publishing Company

Exercise 3

Observe a slide with a cross-section of the small intestine under a microscope. Using the scanning lens, observe the numerous villi extending into the lumen and label these features (villi; lumen) on Fig. 10.10.

Then, increase the magnification to high power and focus on the surface of a single villus. Can you see the brush border?

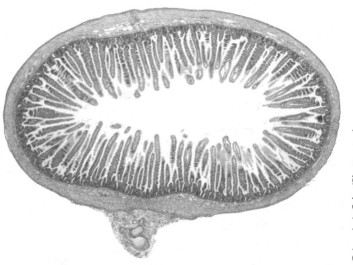

© Jose Luis Calvo/Shutterstock.com

Figure 10.10 Cross-section of the small intestine.

THE LARGE INTESTINE

The **large intestine (LI)** is the 1.5 m (5 ft) long final portion of the alimentary canal extending from where it connects with the ileum to the anus (Fig. 10.1). The LI performs the final processing of chyme and prepares the remaining, undigested feces for elimination through the anus.

Fig. 10.11 shows the many regions of the LI. Chyme from the SI first enters the **cecum**, a large sac-like structure that, in humans and other primates, terminates in a small, twisted tube called the **appendix**. In herbivorous (plant-eating) mammals the cecum holds large amounts of bacteria capable of breaking down the cellulose in plant materials like grass; although humans also have a cecum, they do not possess these bacteria.

Most of the remaining length of the LI is the **colon**, which is further divided into **ascending, transverse, descending,** and **sigmoid** regions (Fig. 10.11). Like other parts of the digestive system, the LI also has both circular and longitudinal muscles that carry out peristalsis. However, in the colon, three conspicuous bands of thickened longitudinal muscles, called *teniae coli,* run most of its length. Their contractions arrange the colon into a series of pouches called *haustra* that give the LI its characteristic bulging appearance. The **rectum** collects feces until stretch receptors in this section signal the need for defecation, the elimination of feces through the **anus**.

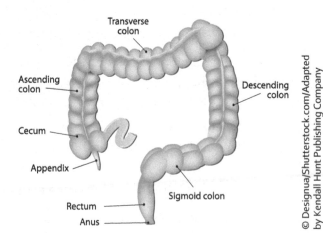

Figure 10.11   Anatomy of the large intestine.

© Designua/Shutterstock.com/Adapted by Kendall Hunt Publishing Company

Although a large amount of water is absorbed by the small intestine, roughly half of the remaining water that enters the LI is absorbed by this organ via osmosis. Along with water, dissolved ions and vitamins are also absorbed, making the water/salt balance of the body a primary function of the LI. The colon also houses the nearly 100 trillion symbiotic bacteria collectively known as the **gut flora**, which contribute to human health and homeostasis through their production of some B vitamins and vitamin K.

CONSIDER FURTHER . . .

1. Food poisoning is caused by ingested bacteria that survive the acidity of the stomach to enter the small intestine and the colon. These bacteria produce toxins that damage cells of the mucosa—the inner lining of these organs. Why is diarrhea (watery stool) a common symptom of food poisoning?

2. Why might the prolonged use of antibiotics result in a vitamin K deficiency?

The salivary glands of the mouth contribute to the digestive process without receiving food directly. Similarly, chyme that enters the duodenum, the first part of the small intestine, mixes with the secretions from the **liver, gallbladder,** and the **pancreas** (Fig. 10.1). These organs are known as the **accessory organs** of the digestive system because they play assisting roles in food processing.

THE LIVER AND GALLBLADDER

The liver is the largest internal organ (by weight) located inferior to the diaphragm on the right side of the abdominal cavity. The liver is divided into a larger right lobe and a smaller left lobe by the *falciform ligament*, a fold in the mesentery tissue that holds and supports the abdominal organs.

The major functional cells of the liver are the **hepatocytes,** which are arranged into long plates only 1–2 cells wide called *hepatic laminae* (Fig. 10.12). On either side of these plates are highly permeable blood capillaries that carry blood past the hepatocytes to drain into larger veins that connect with the inferior vena cava.

The liver contributes to homeostasis in many ways, including:

- Metabolism of lipids and proteins
- Processing of drugs and hormones
- Storage of vitamins
- Regulation of blood sugar
- Synthesis of bile

Hepatocytes can create up to 1 L of bile each day. **Bile** is a solution of water, bile salts, cholesterol, and other substances that serve to **emulsify,** or fragment large lipid globules into much smaller lipid globules for dispersal in aqueous solution. The smaller globules provide pancreatic lipase a much greater surface area for hydrolysis, increasing the efficiency of digestion and absorption of fats and oils.

The **gallbladder** is a small, pear-shaped sac located under the right lobe of the liver. The gallbladder stores and concentrates bile from the liver, releasing it through the common bile duct and into the duodenum as chyme passes (Figure 10.13).

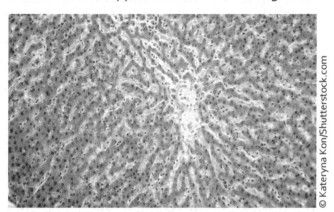

© Kateryna Kon/Shutterstock.com

Figure 10.12   Hepatocytes of the liver. Plates of hepatocytes (stained darker red) are surrounded by capillaries (lighter pink). Blood is carried to central veins (open space at center).

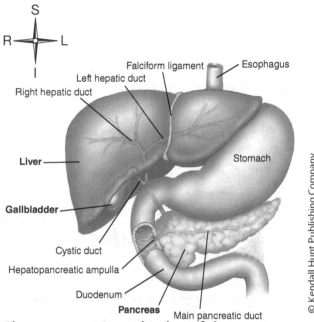

© Kendall Hunt Publishing Company

Figure 10.13   Organization of the accessory organs in the abdominal cavity.

THE PANCREAS

The pancreas is a slender gland that is 12–15 cm (5–6 in.) long and lies posterior to the greater curvature of the stomach (Fig. 10.13). Like the liver, the pancreas also performs multiple functions: the secretion of insulin and glucagon hormones to regulate blood glucose, the production of bicarbonate ion (HCO_3^-) to buffer the low pH of chyme exiting the stomach, and the release of several digestive enzymes into the duodenum.

Each day, the pancreas produces up to 1.5 L of pancreatic juices that enter the duodenum via the pancreatic duct. The **pancreatic juices** consist of water, salts, bicarbonate ions, and digestive enzymes. Bicarbonate ion raises the pH of the acidic chyme from the stomach, stopping the activity of pepsin and allowing the pancreatic and intestinal enzymes to function. The various pancreatic enzymes and their substrates are listed in Table 10.2.

Table 10.2   Various enzymes produced by the pancreas and their functions in the small intestine.

Enzyme	Function
Pancreatic amylase	Digests starch to form monosaccharides
Trypsin, Chymotrypsin, Carboxypeptidase, Elastase	Digests protein to form amino acids
Pancreatic lipase	Digests triglycerides (fats + oils) to form glycerol and fatty acids
Ribonuclease, Deoxyribonuclease	Digests nucleic acids (RNA + DNA) to form nucleotides

? CHECK YOUR UNDERSTANDING

1. Triglycerides are lipids that form large globules in solution because they are _____, or "water-fearing", molecules. As an emulsifier, bile disaggregates these large globules to increase the amount of _____ for pancreatic lipase to conduct hydrolysis.

2. Describe how the cooperation of bile and lipase is similar to the HCl-pepsin interaction in the stomach.

3. What would be the consequences if the pancreatic juices did not contain HCO_3^-?

4. Why do you think the salivary glands, liver, gallbladder, and pancreas are identified as *accessory* organs?

CHAPTER 11
THE URINARY SYSTEM

 Laboratory Objectives

By the end of this laboratory, the student should be able to:

- identify the major organs of the human urinary system;
- recognize the three regions of the kidney: the renal cortex, renal medulla, and renal pelvis;
- identify the different parts of the nephron and know which step in urine formation each part performs;
- describe the events of filtration, reabsorption, and secretion and explain their importance to homeostasis.

The kidneys are responsible for removing waste molecules circulating in the blood through the production of urine. The kidneys are one of the body's major excretory organs along with the skin, liver, and the digestive system. In addition to their roles in excretion, the kidneys also maintain homeostasis by regulating blood pressure, blood volume, and blood pH.

The functional units within the kidneys are millions of small tubules known as **nephrons**, which interact with the blood and surrounding tissues to first filter dissolved substances from the plasma, and then later return most of the water and solutes to the bloodstream. Wastes to be removed include ammonium (NH_4^+), **urea** and uric acid (nitrogen-containing organic molecules), creatinine (a waste product of muscle tissue), and bilirubin (from the breakdown of hemoglobin).

The processing of the filtrate inside the nephron gives the organism careful control over blood composition by regulating what is returned to the bloodstream. The remaining filtrate removed from the plasma eventually becomes the **urine**, which is stored in the bladder until micturition (i.e., urination).

In this lab exercise you will observe models and microscope slides of the mammalian urinary system and learn how the nephron, through the creation of urine, carries out critical functions that help maintain homeostasis.

The urinary system consists of two **kidneys**, two **ureters**, a single **urinary bladder** and one **urethra** (Fig. 11.1). The kidneys filter the blood and process the filtrate to create urine, which is transported through the ureter to enter the urinary bladder. As urine fills the bladder, stretch receptors transmit nerve impulses to the spinal cord as part of the micturition reflex that empties the bladder, sending urine out of the body through the urethra. Although **micturition** (i.e., urination) is a reflex, we learn to control a sphincter muscle surrounding the urethra to either initiate or delay its occurrence.

Exercise 1

View the model of the urinary system on display and use Fig. 11.1 to help familiarize you with the major structures of the urinary system in the human body. Your instructor will indicate which structures are most important for your learning goals.

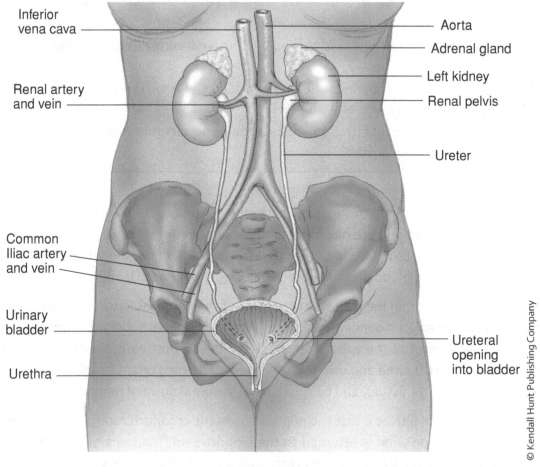

Inferior vena cava

Aorta

Adrenal gland

Left kidney

Renal artery and vein

Renal pelvis

Ureter

Common Iliac artery and vein

Urinary bladder

Ureteral opening into bladder

Urethra

© Kendall Hunt Publishing Company

Figure 11.1   Structures of the human urinary system.

The human kidneys are bean-shaped organs located posterior to the abdominal cavity, which is lined with a continuous tissue layer called the **peritoneum** (Fig. 11.2). The kidneys, like the duodenum and sections of the colon, are known as *retroperitoneal* ("behind the peritoneum") organs.

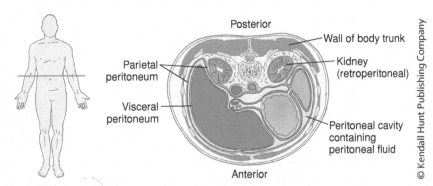

Figure 11.2   Cross-section of the abdominal cavity. The kidneys are held firmly against the body wall by the peritoneum lining the abdominal cavity.

Three areas of the kidney are recognized (Fig. 11.3):

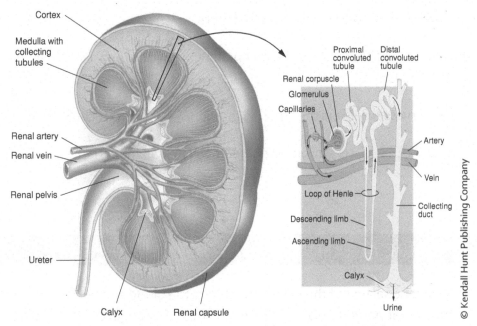

Figure 11.3   Anatomical features of the kidney.

- **Renal cortex**: the outer layer of the kidney that contains the renal corpuscles and much of the renal tubules.
- **Renal medulla**: the darker layer just below the cortex appearing as repeating renal pyramids that consist of nephron loops and collecting ducts.
- **Renal pelvis**: a smooth inner layer that fills with urine from the collecting ducts.

Exercise 2

Study a model of the kidney on display in the laboratory. Use Fig. 11.3 to locate the renal cortex, renal medulla, and renal pelvis. Then, *label each of these regions* on the picture of a kidney shown in Fig. 11.4.

© Rattiya Thongdumhyu/Shutterstock.com

Figure 11.4   Longitudinal section of a kidney.

TEST YOUR KNOWLEDGE

?

1. Which region of the kidney connects to the ureter? _____

2. In which region of the kidney is blood first filtered by the renal corpuscles?
   _____

3. Which blood vessel delivers the blood to the kidney—the **renal artery** or the **renal vein**?
   _____ Is this blood *oxygen-rich* or *oxygen-poor*? _____

11.3 STRUCTURE AND FUNCTIONS OF THE NEPHRON

The nephron is the functional unit of the kidney that filters the blood and produces urine. Nephrons are microscopic tubules (approximately 1 million per kidney) that begin the filtration process in the renal cortex and then travel in and out of the renal medulla as they process the **filtrate** (the materials removed from the blood plasma) to finally create urine to be expelled from the body.

Five areas are important to understanding the structure of the nephron: the **Bowman's capsule**, the **proximal convoluted tubule (PCT)**, the **loop of Henle**, the **distal convoluted tubule (DCT),** and the **collecting duct**.

Multiple nephrons empty into a single collecting duct, which carries the urine into the renal pelvis. Fig. 11.5 shows these structures within two nephrons of different size (longer and shorter loops of Henle). Note how both nephrons are shown emptying into a single collecting duct; also, note the location of these structures within the renal cortex and renal medulla.

The process of creating urine involves three steps: **filtration, reabsorption,** and **secretion**.

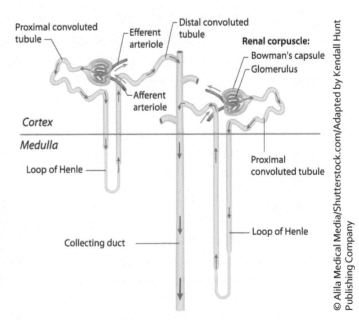

Figure 11.5   Structures of the nephron. Two nephrons of different length are shown connecting to a single collecting duct.

GLOMERULAR FILTRATION

Blood entering the kidney through the renal artery is filtered within the **Bowman's capsule**—a pouch that surrounds a small bundle of blood capillaries known as the **glomerulus**. Together, the Bowman's capsule and the glomerulus form a structure known as the **renal corpuscle** (Fig. 11.6).

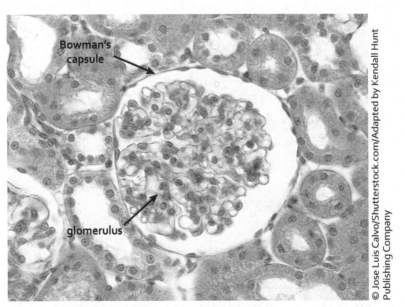

Figure 11.6   The renal corpuscle. In the renal cortex, the glomerulus and the thin cells of the surrounding Bowman's capsule form the renal corpuscle. Portions of the PCT and DCT surround the corpuscle.

The glomerulus is different from most other capillary beds because it is under very high pressure and its endothelium layer has numerous pores; these properties cause water, salts, and small molecules of urea, amino acids, and glucose to pass easily from the plasma into the Bowman's capsule. Because of their larger size, substances like red blood cells and plasma proteins (e.g., albumin) are unable to pass.

Exercise 3

On the picture shown here, draw an arrow from left to right beside the substances that will leave the glomerulus to enter the Bowman's capsule to become the filtrate.

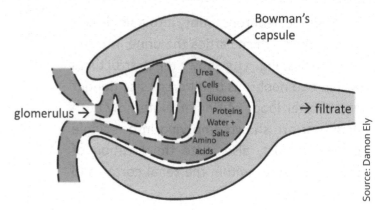

TUBULAR REABSORPTION

Tubular reabsorption is the process by which certain necessary materials are returned to the blood. Reabsorption begins as soon as the filtrate enters the **proximal convoluted tubule (PCT)** (Fig. 11.5). Enough salts and water are passively reabsorbed to *maintain blood volume and blood pressure*, while 100% of glucose, amino acids, and other organic monomers are reabsorbed by PCT cells that use ATP energy to power specialized transport proteins in their cell membranes.

Reabsorption continues as the filtrate travels through the **loop of Henle**—a linear portion of the nephron that extends into the renal medulla, does a hairpin turn, and returns to the renal cortex (Fig. 11.5). As the filtrate travels through the descending portion, water is reabsorbed due to the hypertonic environment of the renal medulla. In the ascending portion, Na^+ and Cl^- are actively pumped into the medulla to maintain its hypertonicity.

A final instance of water reabsorption takes place after the filtrate leaves the distal convoluted tubule and is passing through the **collecting duct**. The cells of the collecting duct are under hormonal control to adjust their permeability to water; thus, at this location the body can carefully control its water balance (and subsequently, its blood volume and blood pressure).

?

APPLY YOUR UNDERSTANDING

1. By what transport process is water being reabsorbed? _____

2. Some salts are passively reabsorbed by traveling through gaps between the cells of the PCT as they move down their concentration gradient. What transport process is at work here? _____

3. Think about the consequences if reabsorption did not take place. Provide a couple of reasons why reabsorption is an essential process for homeostasis.

4. Of all the substances that initially entered the filtrate in Exercise 3, which one do you think is reabsorbed the least? _____

Exercise 4

Observe a microscope slide showing a longitudinal section of a rat kidney and compare it to Fig. 11.7. With help from your instructor, study the differences between the renal cortex and the renal medulla to help you distinguish these two regions from each other. (Look for the many renal corpuscles, which are present in the renal cortex but not in the renal medulla.)

Label a renal corpuscle, the renal cortex, and the renal medulla in Fig. 11.7.

TUBULAR SECRETION

Following the loop of Henle, the filtrate returns to the renal cortex and passes through the final portion of the nephron, the **distal convoluted tubule (DCT)**, where excess amounts of unwanted substances are removed from the body through tubular secretion.

During filtration, only 20% of the passing plasma (and thus, the dissolved wastes) becomes filtrate. Certain substances, like antibiotics, ammonia (NH_3), and hydrogen ions (H^+) must be removed in greater amounts than passive filtration allows. These substances are actively secreted into the DCT before the filtrate enters the collecting duct to become urine.

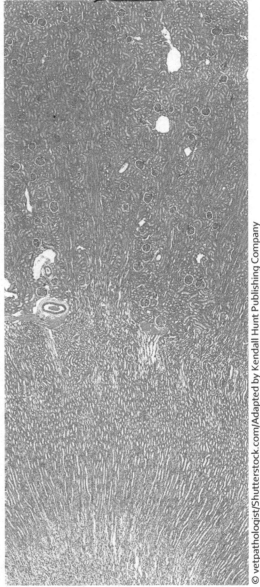

Figure 11.7   Longitudinal section of a rat kidney.

REVIEW OF KIDNEY FUNCTION

?

1. Which step in urine formation helps to maintain blood volume and blood pressure?

2. Which step helps control blood pH?

3. Which step removes the nitrogenous waste urea?

Exercise 5

Use the following diagrams to help you study by providing the missing labels. Fig. 11.8 shows the kidney in longitudinal section. Fig. 11.9 shows the nephron as it appears with surrounding blood vessels, known as the **peritubular capillaries**.

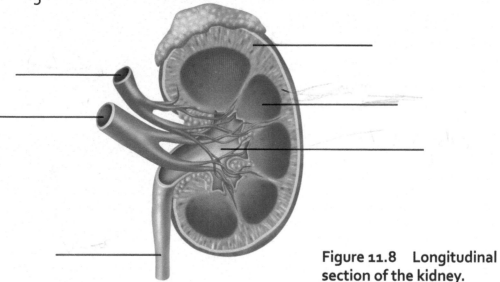

Figure 11.8   Longitudinal section of the kidney.

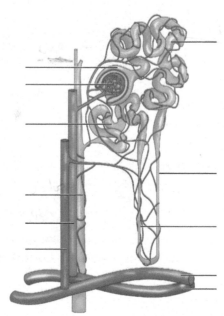

Figure 11.9   Blood vessels surrounding a nephron.

FURTHER REVIEW

1. Trace the path of **blood** from where it leaves the aorta to enter the kidney to where it leaves the kidney to return to the inferior vena cava. Name the structures in correct order.

2. Trace the path of filtrate from where it enters the nephron during the filtration step to where it leaves the body as urine. Name all structures in correct order.

3. Why do you think some animals that live in the desert have very long loops of Henle?

4. Explain why an individual with diabetes (high blood sugar) would have glucose in their urine.

5. Proteinuria occurs when the kidney allows large proteins, like albumin, to be lost in the urine. Which step in urine formation is most likely malfunctioning to cause proteinuria?

CHAPTER 12
NERVOUS AND SENSORY SYSTEMS

 ## Laboratory Objectives

By the end of this laboratory, the student should be able to:

- explain the difference between the central and the peripheral nervous system;
- describe the general structure of a neuron and differentiate among sensory neurons, interneurons, and motor neurons;
- locate and identify different parts of the human brain and provide a brief description of what each part does;
- explain how reflexes work and describe the role of the spinal cord in the reflex arc;
- understand how the nervous system and the sensory system function together to maintain homeostasis;
- locate and identify the different structures of the human eye, ear, and skin.

The brain and the spinal cord make up one division of the nervous system: the **central nervous system (CNS)**. The other division, the **peripheral nervous system (PNS)**, is composed of the cranial nerves and the spinal nerves that extend throughout the body (Fig. 12.1). The PNS carries incoming sensory information in the form of nerve impulses from specialized **sensory receptors** located around the body to the CNS, which integrates the information and determines the correct response. Outgoing nerve impulses are relayed back to the PNS to stimulate effectors (muscles and glands) to generate a response (i.e., a muscle contraction or glandular secretion).

Through the recognition of and response to stimuli, the nervous system and the senses work together to maintain homeostasis.

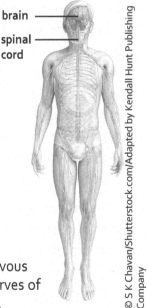

brain
spinal cord

Figure 12.1 The nervous system. The central nervous system is the brain and the spinal cord. All other nerves of the body are part of the peripheral nervous system.

The nervous system is composed of cell types that fall into two major categories: neurons and glial cells. **Neurons** are highly-branched, elongated cells that carry nerve impulses around the body. *Glial cells* do not conduct nerve impulses but instead surround, support, and assist neurons in various ways.

Three types of neurons are involved in the response to a stimulus. **Sensory neurons** gather information from sensory receptors and transmit nerve impulses to the CNS where **interneurons** integrate the information to form a proper response. Interneurons then make **synapses,** or connections, with **motor neurons** that deliver nerve impulses to the muscles and glands needed for the response.

Most neurons share three cellular features: the cell body, dendrites, and an axon (Fig. 12.2). The **cell body** is typically the widest part of the cell that contains the nucleus and many of the other organelles of the eukaryotic cell. The **dendrites** are shorter, highly-branched extensions that receive impulses from sensory cells or other neurons.

Each neuron has a single, long **axon** that propagates the nerve impulse towards another neuron, muscle cell, or gland. The end of an axon branches out to form many *axon terminals.* Many, but not all, axons are covered in a myelin sheath. The **myelin sheath** is an insulating layer

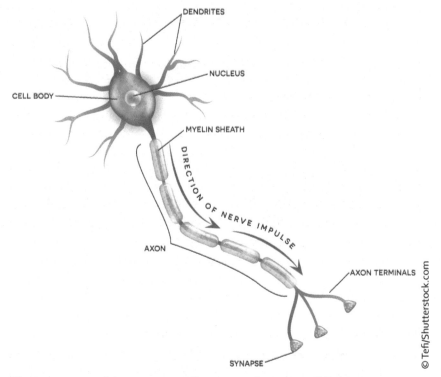

© Tefi/Shutterstock.com

Figure 12.2   The neuron. All neurons have a cell body, dendrites, and a long axon. The motor neuron shown here has a myelin sheath, which covers the axons of peripheral nerves and neurons in the white matter of the CNS.

made up of another cell type that serves to speed up the transmission of a nerve impulse. Neurons that possess a myelin sheath are said to be *myelinated*, those without are *unmyelinated*.

The myelin sheath of peripheral nerves is created by glial cells called *Schwann cells* that wrap around the axon extensively, leaving only small gaps of exposed axon called *Nodes of Ranvier*. Nerve impulses, also known as *action potentials*, can only occur at these nodes, causing action potentials to leap down the axon at high speeds. A motor neuron showing these structural features is pictured in Fig. 12.2.

Exercise 1

Observe the microscope slide showing a neuron smear and compare it to Fig. 12.3. Add the following labels to Fig. 12.3: **cell body, dendrites, axon**. Be sure to observe these structures on the neuron models on display in the laboratory.

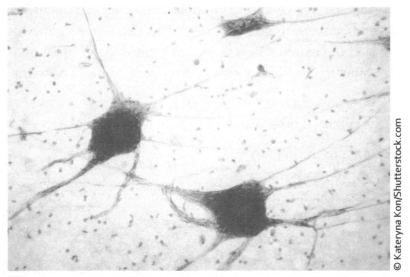

© Kateryna Kon/Shutterstock.com

Figure 12.3   Multipolar neurons. These multipolar neurons have multiple dendrites and a single axon extending directly from the cell body. Many smaller glial cells are visible surrounding the neurons.

12.2   CENTRAL NERVOUS SYSTEM: THE BRAIN AND SPINAL CORD

The **brain** is the anterior portion of the spinal cord; it is housed and protected by the cranium, the upper portion of the skull (Fig. 12.4). The brain is composed of about 100 billion neurons and trillions of glial cells, giving it an overall mass of 1300 grams, or nearly 3 lb, in adults.

The brain acts as the central processing unit for all incoming sensory information. New information is integrated with stored information to make decisions and execute responses via motor functions. Although the brain is a highly interconnected functional unit, we recognize different parts of the brain that carry out particular functions.

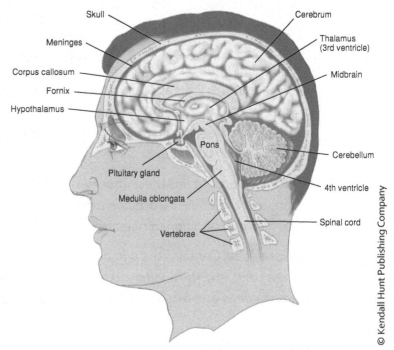

© Kendall Hunt Publishing Company

Figure 12.4   The human brain.

MAJOR PARTS OF THE BRAIN

1. Cerebrum

Called the "seat of intelligence" the cerebrum is highly developed in humans, giving us the ability to read, write, speak, and compose music. The cerebrum is composed of a highly-folded outer layer of gray matter called the **cerebral cortex**, which is divided into right and left halves called *cerebral hemispheres*. Below the cerebral cortex is a band of white matter, the *corpus callosum*, joining the hemispheres.

We further divide the cerebral cortex into four surface lobes (Fig. 12.5):

a) **Frontal lobe**: Contains the *primary motor area* that controls motor functions including voluntary muscle contractions; it also contains *Broca's speech area* for communicating, and the frontal cortex, which contributes to a person's sense of smell, their intellect, personality, problem-solving ability, and conscience.

b) **Parietal lobe**: Contains the *primary somatosensory area* that receives sensory information from the entire body, allowing us to pinpoint the origin of sensations like pain, touch, temperature, itch, and pressure. The parietal lobe also allows you to distinguish tastes, and to compare current sensations with previous experiences (e.g., being able to recognize a tennis ball simply by touching it).

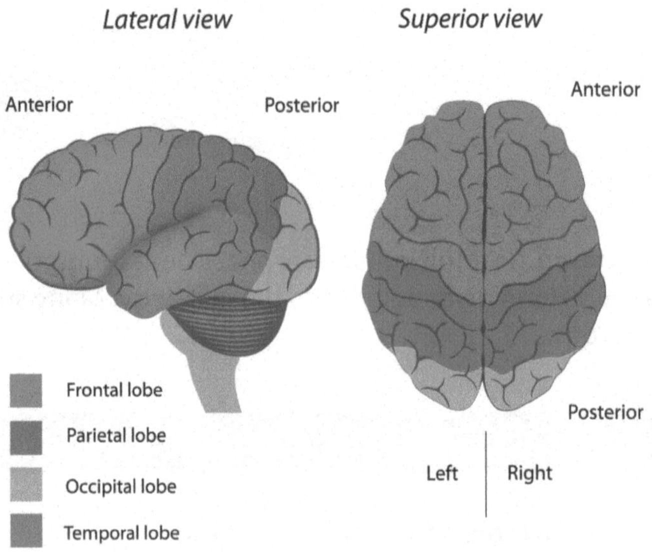

Figure 12.5 The lobes of the cerebral cortex. The cerebral cortex is composed of the frontal, parietal, occipital and temporal lobes, so named for the overlying bones of the skull.

© Alila Medical Media/Shutterstock.com/Adapted by Kendall Hunt Publishing Company

c) **Occipital lobe**: Contains the *primary visual area*, which receives and interprets visual information, and the *visual association area*, which combines present and past visual information to allow recognition of objects when seen.

d) **Temporal lobe**: Contains the *primary auditory area*, which receives and interprets information for sound, and the *auditory association area*. The temporal lobe also contains the *facial recognition area* and receives information from the *olfactory bulb* (i.e., sense of smell).

?

APPLY YOUR UNDERSTANDING

Which lobe of the cerebral cortex:

Helps you distinguish the taste of an onion versus an apple? _____

Helps you hear a plane flying overhead? _____

Helps you solve a math problem? _____

Helps you see the onion, the apple, the plane, and the math problem? _____

2. Diencephalon

The diencephalon is a central region of brain tissue encapsulated by the two cerebral hemispheres. This part of the brain consists of two structures: the thalamus and the hypothalamus, and is also the location of one of the four ventricles (fluid-filled cavities) of the brain.

a) **Thalamus:** A pair of oval masses of gray matter connected by a small bridge of nervous tissue called the *intermediate mass*. The thalamus serves as a relay station for incoming sensory information, controlling which messages get passed on to the cerebrum. The thalamus also transmits information from the cerebellum to the primary motor areas of the cerebral cortex.

b) **Hypothalamus:** The hypothalamus is inferior to the thalamus and projects anteriorly; the end of the hypothalamus connects with the *pituitary gland* by a small stem called the *infundibulum*. This area of the diencephalon is heavily influential over homeostasis in the following ways:

   i.   It monitors blood glucose levels, concentrations of hormones, and blood temperature.
   ii. It contains centers that promote urges to eat and drink, and causes the sensation of fullness.
   iii. It serves as the body's thermostat to control body temperature.
   iv. It establishes circadian rhythms, daily patterns of biological activity like waking and sleeping.
   v.   It is an important point of connection between the nervous and endocrine systems. The hypothalamus creates hormones that govern the pituitary gland, which in turn governs many of the major endocrine glands of the body.
   vi. It regulates emotional and behavior patterns such as rage, pain, pleasure, and sexual arousal.

3. Cerebellum

The cerebellum is a large portion of the brain (10% of total brain mass) attached to the dorsal side of the brain stem and inferior to the occipital lobe (Figure 12.4). Like the cerebral cortex, the cerebellum is also highly folded to increase surface area and the number of neurons (the cerebellum contains almost half of all the neurons of the brain!).

The cerebellum ensures that the motor activities initiated by the cerebrum are carried out correctly and smoothly. The cerebellum communicates with the cerebrum through the thalamus to correct errors in motor activities and to coordinate highly complex movements by the skeletal muscles. In addition, posture and balance are also regulated to maintain an individual's equilibrium.

4. Brain Stem

The brain stem connects the spinal cord to the diencephalon and is made up of three structures: the medulla oblongata, the pons, and the midbrain (Fig. 12.4).

a) **Medulla oblongata**: Also known as the medulla, this portion of the brain stem is continuous with the superior end of the spinal cord. The medulla contains the cardiovascular and respiratory centers which regulate the rate and force of the heartbeat and the rhythm of breathing. The medulla also controls reflexes for sneezing, hiccupping, vomiting, and swallowing.

b) **Pons:** The pons appears as a conspicuous bulging portion of the brain stem superior to the medulla. Numerous tracts of myelinated neurons in the pons provide critical connections between the medulla, the cerebellum, and the higher brain regions.

c) **Midbrain:** The midbrain connects the pons to the diencephalon and thus serves as another relay center for sensory input and motor output. The midbrain is part of neural circuits that are responsible for reflexes that govern eye movements (dilation of pupils, focusing of the lens), head and trunk movements (e.g., the *startle reflex*), as well as other subconscious muscle activities.

Familiarize yourself with the parts of the brain by viewing the models on display in the laboratory and by looking at Fig. 12.4. Then, *apply labels to this image of the brain* using the following terms: **brain stem; medulla; pons; midbrain; cerebellum; diencephalon; thalamus; hypothalamus; pituitary gland; cerebrum**.

Exercise 2

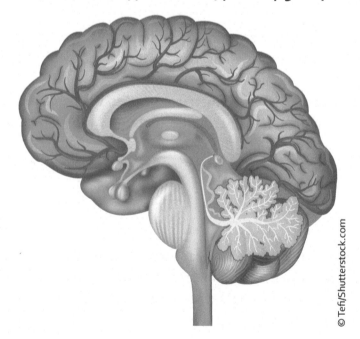

© Tefi/Shutterstock.com

TEST YOUR KNOWLEDGE

?

Identify the part of the brain best described by the following:

1. Control center for appetite, body temperature, and pain _____

2. Coordinates complex movements and equilibrium _____

3. Most developed brain area; primary motor and sensory areas _____

4. Transmits information between medulla and higher regions _____

5. Regulates heart rate, breathing, sneezing, and vomiting _____

6. Controls impulses to the cerebrum _____

7. Relay for sensory input/motor output; controls eye movement _____

Exercise 3

Observe the sheep brain on display in the laboratory. With the help of Fig. 12.6 and your studies thus far, identify as many features of the brain as you can on the specimen.

Wear protective gloves and eyewear when handling preserved animal organs and use caution if you are using any sharp dissecting equipment.

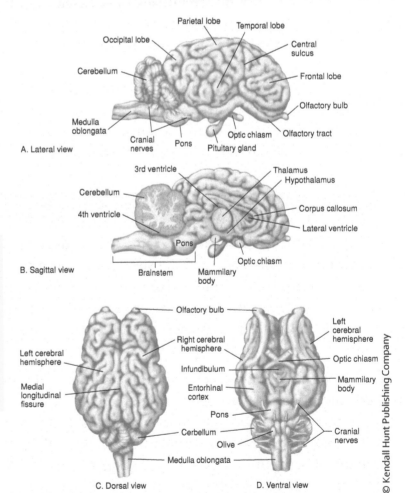

Figure 12.6   The sheep brain.

© Kendall Hunt Publishing Company

THE SPINAL CORD

The **spinal cord** extends from below the brain stem to our abdominal region and is surrounded and protected by the vertebral column. The spinal cord is responsible for many of our nervous reflexes (i.e., responses independent of the brain), it carries sensory information from the peripheral nerves of the body toward the brain, and it carries motor information from the brain back out to the body.

Exercise 4

Observe the microscope slide of the mammalian spinal cord under the lowest magnification, the scanning lens. Use Fig. 12.7 along with the descriptions below to familiarize yourself with the structures and functions of the spinal cord.

The spinal cord is composed of an outer layer of myelinated neurons called **white matter**. White matter appears white because of the myelin sheaths that cover the long axons that travel up and down this region of the spinal cord. These axons carry impulses to and from the brain.

A central, butterfly-shaped area called **gray matter** lies inside of the white matter. This layer contains unmyelinated neurons that are part of the spinal reflex arc; these shorter neurons

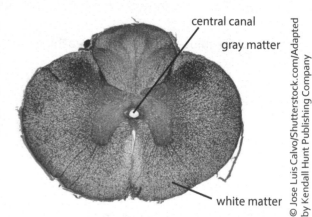

© Jose Luis Calvo/Shutterstock.com/Adapted by Kendall Hunt Publishing Company

Figure 12.7   Cross-section of the spinal cord.

only transverse the width of the spinal cord. At the center of the gray matter is the **central canal**, a long narrow tube filled with *cerebrospinal fluid* that carries nutrients and provides protection from an impact.

12.3 PERIPHERAL NERVOUS SYSTEM

The peripheral nervous system is composed of the nerves that arise from the brain and the spinal cord and extend throughout the body. Cranial nerves arise from areas of the brain and serve the head region of the body. Spinal nerves project from both left and right sides of the spinal cord to serve the rest of the body (Fig. 12.1).

Nerves are composed of the myelinated axons of sensory and motor neurons bundled together with glial cells in layers of connective tissue (Fig. 12.8). Sensory neurons carry nerve impulses to the spinal cord and, depending on the stimulus, the message will either be sent to the brain to be integrated, or integration will occur directly in the spinal cord to produce a motor response.

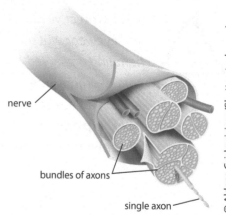

© Aldona Griskeviciene/Shutterstock.com/ Adapted by Kendall Hunt Publishing Company

Figure 12.8   Structure of a nerve.

THE REFLEX ARC

Reflexes are involuntary responses such as those that involve only the spinal cord; the path traveled by the nerve impulses forming a reflex is called the **reflex arc** (Fig. 12.9).

Exercise 5

Study Fig. 12.9 by reading through the following description of a reflex and answering questions along the way. Observe the model of the reflex arc on display and identify the parts you recognize in Fig. 12.9.

Suppose you accidentally touch a very hot surface, or that you are stung by a flying insect. You know that your reflex is to pull away from the source of the stimulus, often before you know you have even done so.

- Place the following terms in the correct order traveled by nerve impulses to generate this response: **interneuron, muscle cell, sensory neuron, motor neuron, pain receptor.**

1. _____ → 2. _____ → 3. _____ → 4. _____ → 5. _____

Sensory and motor neurons are bundled together in the nerve except where it splits into a *dorsal root* and a *ventral root* at its connection with the spinal cord.

- Which type of neuron branches into the dorsal root? _____
- Which type of neuron branches into the ventral root? _____
- *Ganglia* are bulges outside of the CNS caused by an accumulation of cell bodies. Which type of neuron forms ganglia? _____

The sensory neuron axon synapses with an interneuron in the gray matter of the spinal cord. The interneuron then synapses with a motor neuron that carries the nerve impulse back out to a muscle cell, stimulating it to contract and pull away that part of the body.

- Is the interneuron myelinated or unmyelinated? _____
- Why can the organism afford *not* to cover interneurons in the reflex arc with a myelin sheath? _____

_____

_____

- What *advantage* is provided to the organism by having unmyelinated interneurons in the reflex arc? _____

_____

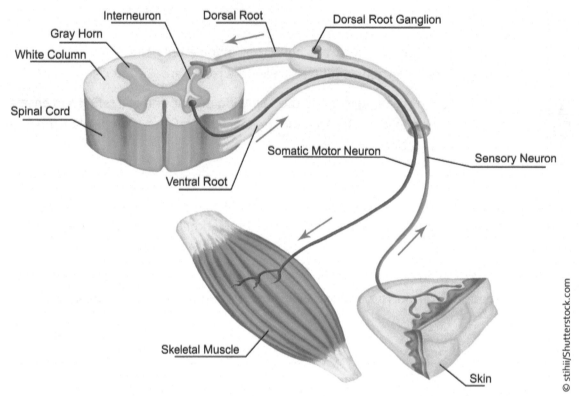

Figure 12.9   The reflex arc. Quick, involuntary responses to stimuli often involve integration in the spinal cord that directs a motor response without help from the brain.

Exercise 6

The knee-jerk (patellar) reflex is a common test to ensure nervous system health. When the patellar tendon is tapped, stretch receptors signal the change, which results in the contraction of the leg muscle. Reflexes like this constantly adjust the body's position to maintain balance.

Test the Knee-Jerk Reflex

1. Sit on the edge of a table and let your legs hang freely.
2. Have another student gently tap your patellar tendon, located just below the kneecap, with the flat side of the reflex hammer. See your instructor for guidance.
3. Observe the reaction of your leg, which should extend automatically as part of the reflex.

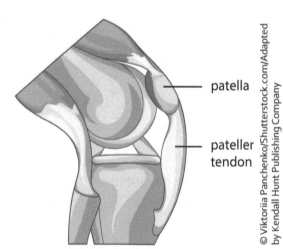

Figure 12.10   The patellar tendon in the knee.

REACTION TIME

Responses to stimuli that are consciously initiated are called **voluntary reactions**. The time it takes for a voluntary reaction to a stimulus (i.e., the reaction time) varies and depends on the sense organs involved. For example, the receptor cells in muscles that inform the brain about the position of body parts are among the fastest, sending impulses at a speed of nearly 400 feet per second, while (surprisingly) impulses for temperature and pain can be the slowest.

Exercise 7

Measure your reaction time

1. While seated, have your lab partner stand in front of you holding a meter stick at the 100-cm end between their thumb and forefinger. The 0-cm end of the meter stick should be free in the air directly in front of you.

2. Place your thumb and forefinger about an inch apart on either side of the 0-cm end as in Fig. 12.11. Your focus should be on the ruler at your fingertips.

3. Tell your partner when you are ready. Without announcement, your lab partner should let go of the ruler within 10 seconds. As quickly as you can, catch the ruler between your thumb and forefinger.

Figure 12.11
Measuring reaction time.

4. Record the distance the ruler fell (in cm) where you caught it and then repeat the experiment four more times for a total of five readings. Record these distances in Table 12.1 and then calculate the average distance.

5. Use the following equation to determine your average reaction time:

$$t = \sqrt{d \div 4.9}$$

where t is the reaction time in seconds, and d is the average distance in cm.

Table 12.1   Reaction time data.

	Distance (cm)
Trial 1	
Trial 2	
Trial 3	
Trial 4	
Trial 5	
Average	
Reaction Time:	$t = \sqrt{d \div 4.9}$ = _____ SEC

INVESTIGATE FURTHER . . .

Complete the test twice more (5 trials each), this time with different variables that may affect your reaction time. Before you begin, read through each of the tests and make predictions about what, if any, effect these variables (distraction, auditory cue) will have on reaction time. Then complete the tests and enter your results in Table 12.2.

Test 1—Distraction

Question: Will your reaction time differ if you are focused on some other task while doing the test?

Method: Set up the test and begin naming U.S. states out loud (or musicians, or TV shows, etc. . . .) before your partner randomly releases the ruler.

Test 2—Auditory Cue

Question: Will your reaction time differ if your cue (i.e., your stimulus) is auditory instead of visual?

Method: Set up the test and close your eyes. Instruct your partner to say "GO!" at the moment that they randomly release the ruler.

For each test, predict whether reaction time will increase, decrease, or stay the same:

Distraction: _____

Auditory Cue: _____

Table 12.2   Effect of different variables on reaction time.

	Test 1—Distraction Distance (cm)	Test 2—Auditory Cue Distance (cm)
Trial 1		
Trial 2		
Trial 3		
Trial 4		
Trial 5		
Average distance		
Reaction Time (seconds)		

Compare these results to the reaction time you calculated in Table 12.1 and state your conclusions:

_____

_____

_____

The human **eye** is a sense organ of the body that adapted to perceive light rays with wavelengths of 400–700 nanometers (Fig. 12.12). Some other animals, like many invertebrates, have eyes that can see infrared and ultraviolet light.

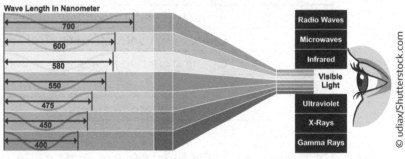

Figure 12.12 Wavelengths of light visible to the human eye.

The eye contains millions of specialized **photoreceptors**—cells that generate a nerve impulse when stimulated by light. The two types of photoreceptors—**rod cells** responsible for black-and-white vision and **cone cells** responsible for color-vision—are embedded in a layer of tissue at the back of the eye known as the **retina**. These cells synapse with neurons that carry information to the brain via the **optic nerve**. Other structures of the eye are responsible for controlling the amount of light that enters and focusing the image.

Exercise 8

Observe the eye model on display and compare it with Fig. 12.13. To help you learn the eye, trace the path of light through the eye and describe the function of each structure along the way. The various structures of the eye and their functions are listed in Table 12.3.

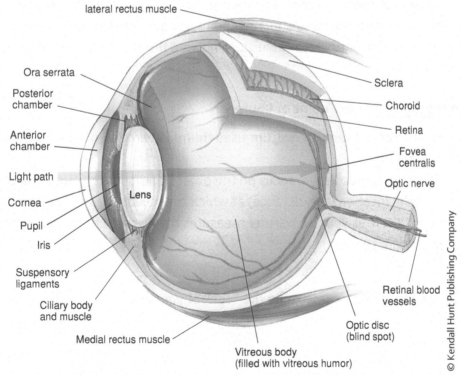

Figure 12.13 Parts of the human eye.

Table 12.3   Parts of the human eye and their associated functions.

Part	Function
Cornea	Refracts (bends) incoming light rays
Iris	Dilates and contracts to control amount of entering light
Pupil	Opening created by iris; allows light entrance
Lens	Curves and flattens to focus light rays
Retina	Contains photoreceptors
Optic Nerve	Carries nerve impulses to brain
Sclera	Outer surface of eye; muscle attachment and protection
Choroid	Vascular layer that delivers oxygen and nourishment
Fovea	Allows highly-detailed vision; area of retina with most cone cells

ACCOMMODATION BY THE LENS

The **lens** is a thin layer of transparent cells behind the iris and pupil (Fig. 12.13). The cells are filled with layers of proteins that refract light to focus images onto the retina. The lens changes its curvature depending on the distance from the observer to the focal object. The change in shape of the lens is called **accommodation**. When the observer tries to focus on a near object, the lens must curve greatly to bend the incoming light rays. The constant bending of the lens causes it to lose some elasticity with age (known as *presbyopia*) making it difficult to focus on near objects.

Exercise 9

The closest distance at which the eye can focus on an object is called the **near point**. Have your partner measure your near point using the methods described below. Then, compare your near point to Table 12.4 showing the standard correlation between age and near point.

To measure the near point of your eye:

1. Hold an object (pen, pencil, upraised thumb) at arm's length in front of the eye you are testing.
2. Close the opposite eye, focus on the object, and begin to move the object closer.
3. Find the location (the distance) at which the object goes out of focus and hold the object there as your lab partner measures the distance from your eye to the object in cm using a meter stick.

near point (cm): _____

4. Use Table 12.4 to determine the "age" of your eye.

Table 12.4   Standard relationship between age and near point.

Age (years)	10	20	30	40	50	60
Near point (cm)	8	9	11	17	52	83

THE BLIND SPOT

The **blind spot** is located at the back of the eye where the optic nerve leaves the retina and there are no photoreceptors. The following exercise will produce evidence of the blind spot in each eye.

Exercise
10

Using the images that appear below, test for your blind spot with the following method.

To test your blind spot:

1. Hold this page about 30 cm in front of you with the star directly in front of your right eye.
2. Close/cover your left eye and slowly bring the page closer to you. Make sure you only stare at the star; you should still be able to see the heart in your field of vision.
3. Without looking away from the star, you should find that the heart disappears from your peripheral vision at some point. At this location, the light rays from the image are striking your blind spot. The brain is compensating for this lack of information by making this part of the page the same background color as the rest of the page.
4. Repeat the test for your left eye in the same way, but focus on the heart and watch for the star to disappear.

The human **ear** is a collection of structures that collect and amplify sound waves to stimulate **mechanoreceptors** called **hair cells** that respond to mechanical/physical manipulation and then send nerve impulses to the brain. The ear also uses mechanoreceptors to maintain gravitational and rotational equilibrium, helping the body to balance itself. The ear is organized into three regions: the **outer, middle,** and **inner** ear.

Exercise 11

Observe the ear model on display and compare it with Fig. 12.14. To help you learn the ear, trace the path of sound through the ear and describe the function of each structure along the way. The various structures of the ear and their functions are listed in Table 12.5.

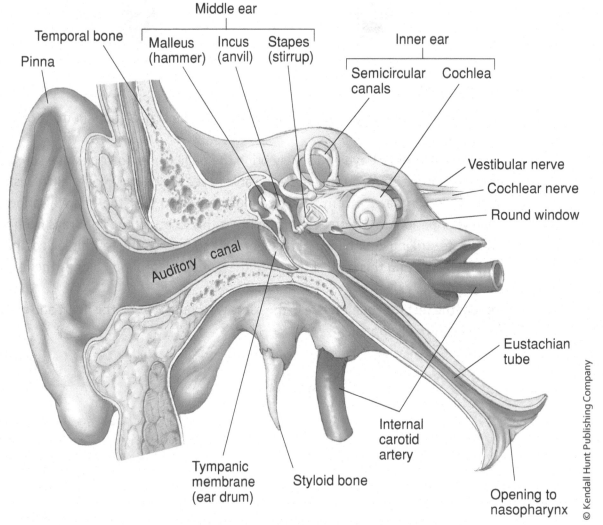

Figure 12.14   Parts of the human ear.

© Kendall Hunt Publishing Company

Table 12.5   Parts of the human ear.

Part	Description
Outer Ear	
Pinna	Flap of elastic cartilage; funnels soundwaves into auditory canal
Auditory Canal	Narrow tube in temporal bone; carries soundwaves to eardrum
Tympanic Membrane	Thin partition that vibrates with soundwaves; vibrates ossicles
Middle Ear	
Ossicles	Three tiny bones (hammer, anvil, stirrup) that amplify sound 20-fold
Eustachian Tube	Connects to nasopharynx; equalizes air pressure in middle ear
Inner Ear	
Cochlea	Spiral tube holding mechanoreceptors (hair cells) for sound
Vestibule (Saccule and Utricle)	Portion of bony labyrinth; holds mechanoreceptors for gravitational equilibrium
Semicircular Canals	Portion of bony labyrinth; holds mechanoreceptors for rotational equilibrium
Cochlear Nerve	Carries nerve impulses from inner ear to brain

Exercise 12

We determine the location of a sound using both ears by how well the sound reaches each of them. Even slight differences in the hearing ability between ears can alter our judgement of the direction from which a sound originates. Do the following to test your lab partner:

Have your partner sit still with eyes closed. Obtain a tuning fork and strike it gently, then hold it in one of the following locations (randomize the order) and ask them to give the location of the sound, record their answer.

Directly in front of their face   Stated location: _____

Directly to their right   Stated location: _____

Directly above their head   Stated location: _____

Directly behind their head   Stated location: _____

Behind and below their head   Stated location: _____

Is there evidence for a difference between your partner's ears? _____

The **skin** is the largest organ of the body both by weight and area and is part of the integumentary system that also includes the hair, nails, oil and sweat glands, and sensory receptors for touch and pressure (Fig. 12.15).

The skin is composed of two major layers, the upper epidermis and a deeper layer, the dermis. The **epidermis** is divided into a surface layer of dead cells and an underlying living layer. The epidermal cells produce substances that protect the skin from abrasions, UV light, heat, and microbes, and they secrete waterproofing chemicals to both retain and repel water. Some epidermal cells called *Merkel cells* synapse with sensory neurons in the dermis and respond to sensations of touch.

The **dermis** is much thicker than the epidermis and consists mostly of connective tissue that is highly flexible. Where the dermis meets the epidermis, tiny projections called **dermal papillae** extend upwards to greatly increase the surface area of this region, known as the *papillary region*. It is here that numerous free nerve endings (the dendrites of sensory neurons) for pain, temperature, itching, and tickling sensations are located along with many receptors for touch.

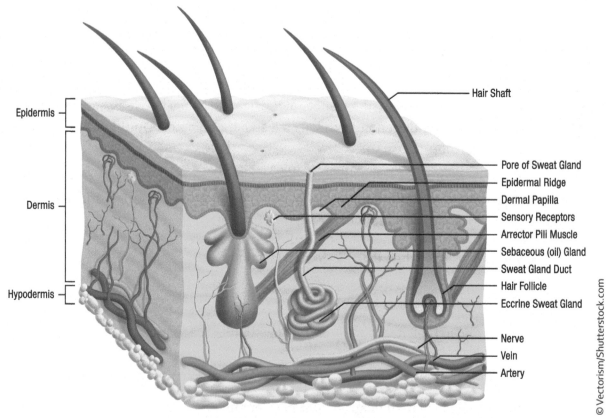

Figure 12.15   **The human integument.**

© Vectorism/Shutterstock.com

INVESTIGATION: DIFFERENCES IN TOUCH SENSITIVITY

Answer the following questions before starting Exercise 13:

1. Which areas of the skin are the most sensitive? Arrange the following locations into order from least to most sensitive: **Back of the neck, Back of the hand, Index finger, Forearm**

   Least ⟶ _____ _____ _____ _____ ⟶ Most

2. If two areas of the skin differ in their sensitivity, what is the underlying cause for this difference?

   _____

Exercise 13

Work with another lab partner to perform this experiment. Record your data in the spaces below.

1. The subject should be seated with eyes closed.

2. For each of the locations, hold the two points of a pair of lab scissors (with fine points) far apart and have them touch the skin area at the same time. The subject will announce whether they feel one or two points contacting their skin.

3. Make the distance between the points shorter and repeat the test in the same skin area. The experimenter should sometimes only press one point to the skin to ensure that the subject makes the determination based only on sensitivity.

4. Keep decreasing the distance between the points and contacting the skin until the subject can no longer distinguish between one or two points. Record the shortest distance between the two points that the subject could still make a two-point determination.

   Back of the neck: _____ mm   Back of the hand: _____ mm

   Index finger: _____ mm   Forearm: _____ mm

INTERPRET YOUR RESULTS

1. How do your results compare to your predictions?

2. Which area appears to have the greatest density of touch receptors?

3. Consider the fact that the nervous system consumes a large portion of your daily energy. Why does it benefit an organism to have less sensitivity in certain areas of the skin?

CHAPTER 13
DISSECTION OF THE FROG

 Laboratory Objectives

By the end of this laboratory, the student should be able to:

- identify external morphological features and the major organs of the cardiovascular, respiratory, digestive, urinary, and reproductive systems in a dissected frog specimen;
- compare the anatomy of the frog to the human anatomy.

The frog is a common specimen for dissection because of its ease of collection, small size, and easily-distinguished anatomical features. Although there are numerous differences from the human body, the frog's anatomy has enough similarity to provide a tangible experience to learn about the major organ systems.

In this laboratory, you will dissect the bullfrog (*Lithobates catesbeianus*) which, like other amphibians, undergoes metamorphosis as part of its life cycle. As a juvenile tadpole it lives entirely underwater, without limbs and breathing through gills. As it matures, a tadpole develops legs and lungs while losing its tail, eventually breathing air and becoming an adult frog (Fig. 13.1).

- *USE CAUTION when handling scalpels, dissecting scissors, and sharp probes during this lab exercise.*
- *You must wear laboratory gloves.*
- *Notify the instructor immediately if any injuries occur, no matter how small.*
- *Locate the first aid kit before starting.*

Source: Damon Ely

Figure 13.1 Frogs are amphibious. This aquatic green frog (*Lithobates clamitans*) displays traits like large forward-looking eyes, external nares, and unwebbed front phalanges that aid it on land.

Obtain a mature bullfrog from your instructor and place it dorsal side up in your dissecting tray. Familiarize yourself with the following external features as shown in Figure 13.2: **forelimb, hind-limb, phalanges, eye, tympanic membrane** (or, *tympanum*). You may notice two incisions on your specimen where it was injected with blue and red solid-forming latex into its venous and arterial systems, respectively.

As you observe your frog, take note of the following features:

- The front phalanges are fewer in number than the hind phalanges.
- The hind phalanges are webbed but the front phalanges are not.
- The **cloacal opening** is visible on the frog's trunk between the hind limbs.
- There is a difference in coloration between the dorsal and ventral sides of the frog.

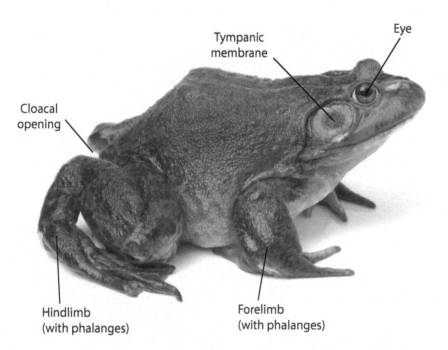

© JIANG HONGYAN/Shutterstock.com/Adapted by Kendall Hunt Publishing Company

Figure 13.2   External features of the bullfrog.

FEATURES OF THE HEAD

Figure 13.3 shows the structural features of the head; use this figure to locate and learn the structures as you read through this section.

1. Observe the eyes of your frog and locate the **nictitating membrane**, a semi-transparent membrane that rises to keep the eye moistened and clean and to cover the eye during diving. Use your blunt probe to find the nictitating membrane if it is not already visible.

2. Posterior to the eye, locate the large, round **tympanic membrane**. This structure, like your eardrum, senses mechanical vibrations—both soundwaves and disturbances in the water (see how the frog rests with the tympanic membrane partially submerged in Fig. 13.1).

3. On the snout, locate the two small **external nares**. These passageways allow air to enter the mouth to be passed into the respiratory system. On the midline between the eyes locate the **brow spot**, a pale dot that is thought to be the remnant of an ancestral "third eye" that was sensitive to light.

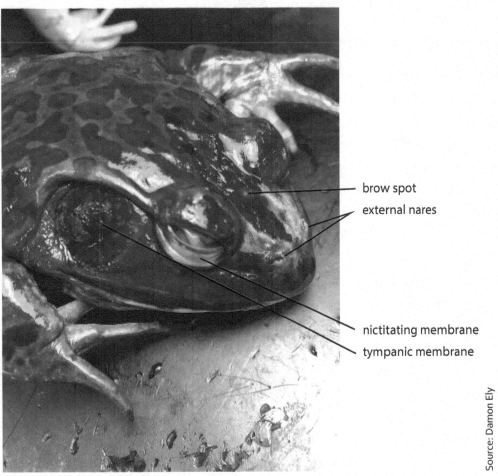

brow spot
external nares
nictitating membrane
tympanic membrane

Source: Damon Ely

Figure 13.3 Structures of the frog's head.

INSIDE THE MOUTH

To open your frog's mouth, you or your instructor may need to cut the jaws. Use Fig. 13.4 and the procedure below to help you identify the following structures: *internal nares, maxillary teeth, vomerine teeth, tongue, esophagus, glottis, Eustachian tubes.*

1. Examine the **tongue** of the frog, which is attached anteriorly with the tip projecting backwards. In life, the tongue is highly elastic and can extend to momentarily stun prey.

2. Observe the beginning of the **esophagus** at the back of the mouth. The skin is highly folded in this area to allow stretching for swallowing prey whole.

3. Lightly trace your finger around the edge of the upper jaw to feel the many small **maxillary teeth**. This serrated edge of the upper jaw helps the frog grip its prey.

4. Gently press your finger against the roof of the mouth to feel the larger **vomerine teeth**. These teeth project inward to prevent escape of the prey.

5. Examine the **internal nares** located alongside the vomerine teeth. These air passages are continuous with the external nares (you can verify this with a sharp probe).

6. Find the **glottis** just anterior to the opening of the esophagus. The glottis is firmly closed to prevent entry of food into the airway. The frog pushes air from its mouth through the glottis to enter the respiratory system.

7. Locate the **Eustachian tubes** at the posterior end of the upper jaw. These passageways connect to the tympanum to equalize changes in air pressure.

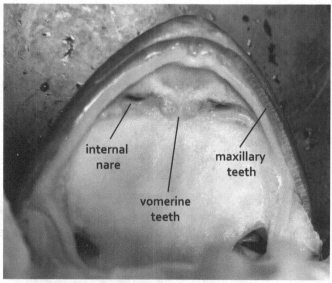

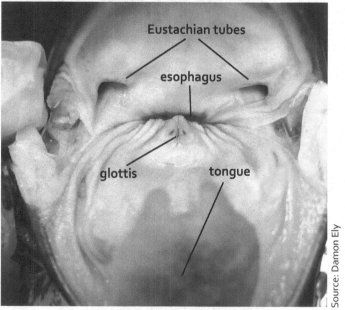

Figure 13.4 Structures of the mouth.

Source: Damon Ely

EXPOSING THE BODY CAVITY

1. Place your frog with its ventral side facing up.

2. Find the incision for the latex injection on the frog's chest and begin cutting with your scissors. Remove the layers of skin and muscle to expose the body cavity and organs.

3. Continue cutting until you have removed the skin and muscle entirely from the abdomen so that the organs are exposed. You will need to do this in the throat/lower jaw area as well, which requires that you cut through the bone of the pectoral girdle. Using your scissors, cut straight up through the midline between the front limbs to the middle of the jaw; apply extra pressure to cut through the bone. After you make this cut, spread the two halves of the pectoral girdle apart to expose the heart.

4. If you have a female with ovaries full of eggs you will need to remove the ovaries and possibly the oviducts before continuing with your dissection. These structures can fill the body cavity, obstructing your view of the other organs. The female frog has two ovaries that develop thousands of tiny black and white eggs. The ovaries are tightly-folded and surrounded by the oviducts, which swell to form very thick tubes (Fig. 13.5).

   - Gently move the visceral organs around to loosen them and find the base of attachment for each ovary.
   - Carefully cut the ovaries' attachment points with the scalpel to remove each ovary.
   - Remove the oviducts.

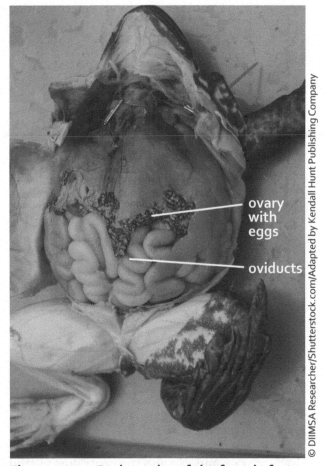

ovary with eggs

oviducts

© DIIMSA Researcher/Shutterstock.com/Adapted by Kendall Hunt Publishing Company

Figure 13.5 Body cavity of the female frog showing the ovaries and oviducts.

1. Locate the central **heart** just anterior to the large, multi-lobed liver (Fig. 13.6). The heart may still be covered in a thin transparent tissue—this is the *pericardium*, a sac that surrounds the heart. You will probably first notice the single large **ventricle** which tapers to a point. Above the ventricle you should be able to distinguish two atria: the **right atrium** and the **left atrium**.

2. Find the **truncus arteriosus**, a thick artery leaving the heart that branches into a Y-shape just anterior to the atria. Oxygen-rich and oxygen-poor blood from the atria partially mixes in the ventricle and leaves the heart via the *truncus arteriosus*. This artery divides the blood between the pulmonary and systemic circuits.

3. Locate the right and left **lungs** (Fig. 13.7) by lifting the liver up and over to one side and then the other. The lungs will appear as small sacs.

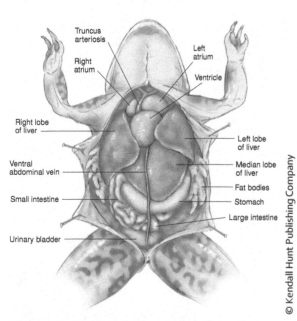

Figure 13.6 Heart, liver, and digestive organs.

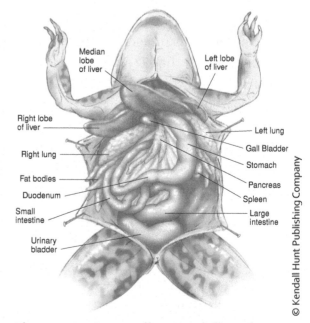

Figure 13.7 Lungs, liver, and digestive organs.

DIGESTIVE SYSTEM

Use Figs. 13.6 and 13.7 and the procedures listed below to locate the following digestive organs and accessory organs: *stomach, small intestine, large intestine, liver, gallbladder,* and *pancreas*.

1. The reddish-brown **liver** is composed of 3 large lobes. Lift the right lobe of the liver to reveal the **gallbladder**.

2. Find the large, curved **stomach** on the frog's left. The curvature of the stomach is like the human and your frog may still have its last meal inside. Cut open the stomach to observe the *rugae*, numerous folds that allow for expansion.

3. Find the **pancreas** by looking in the thin tissues around the inner curve of the stomach. The pancreas appears as a thin, strap-like organ.

4. Examine the **small intestine**, which extends from the base of the stomach. The first portion of the small intestine (SI), the **duodenum**, differs in appearance from the rest of this organ. Notice how the gallbladder and the pancreas connect to the duodenum.

5. Spread the SI out and observe the numerous blood vessels in the thin tissues surrounding the SI. The high degree of vascularization aids absorption.

6. Cut open a section of the SI and observe the many **villi** (the inside surface appears fuzzy) that increase surface area for absorption.

7. Follow the SI until it abruptly enlarges near the posterior end of the frog to become the **large intestine**. See how the large intestine meets the body wall to form the cloacal opening.

UROGENITAL SYSTEM

Figs. 13.8 and 13.9 show the urogenital system of the female and male frog, respectively. Use these figures to locate, on your specimen, the structures described in the procedures below. Make sure to observe another group's specimen of the opposite sex.

1. Look behind the intestines (or remove them) to reveal the two **kidneys** pressed against the dorsal wall of the body cavity. The **posterior vena cava** will appear as a large blood vessel directly between the kidneys with many branching extensions.

2. Look closely for the thin **ureter** extending from each kidney to join the large **urinary bladder**. The bladder appears as a broad, thin sac of tissue surrounding the large intestine where it meets the body wall.

3. The gonads (reproductive organs) are located ventral to the kidneys for both sexes and are surrounded by numerous **fat bodies** that store fat as an energy resource. The **ovaries** and **oviducts** were located earlier and possibly removed as previously instructed. The **testes** of the male appear as two small, smooth, bean-shaped organs attached to each kidney.

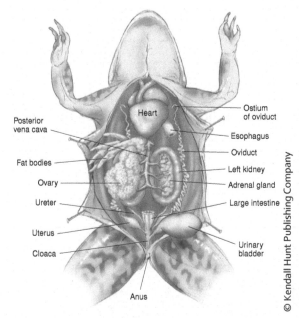

Figure 13.8 Female urogenital organs.

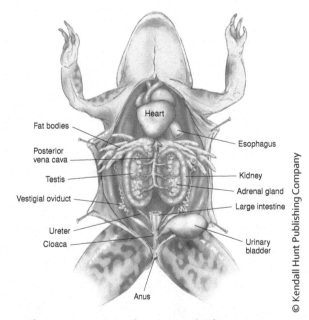

Figure 13.9 Male urogenital organs.

Dispose of any loose organs or tissues into a designated viscera container; return your frog to the specimen bag. Scrub your tray and dissecting instruments with soapy water and leave to air-dry. Disinfect your tabletop using the cleaner available in the laboratory.

REVIEW QUESTIONS

?

1. Which structural features aid the frog when it is in the aquatic environment? Name each feature and write a brief explanation of how it helps.

webbed lower extremities

2. Suppose a frog is resting in the water as in Fig. 13.1 and a flying insect falls in the water nearby and is struggling on the surface. Explain the sequence of events that will follow, ending with the insect prey entering the frog's esophagus. Be sure to describe the use of as many anatomical structures as you can.

3. The frog has a heart that pumps blood through pulmonary and systemic circuits. Describe the ways in which the frog heart and the path of blood out of the heart differs from humans.

4. Which features of the frog digestive system did you find to be very different from humans?

Which features were very similar?

CHAPTER 14
DNA BIOLOGY

 Laboratory Objectives

By the end of this laboratory, the student should be able to:
- describe the structure of the DNA molecule and how it differs from RNA;
- explain the semiconservative process of DNA replication and the major enzymes involved;
- understand how DNA stores information;
- explain how transcription and translation creates a functional protein during gene expression.

Deoxyribonucleic acid, or DNA, belongs to the group of organic molecules known as nucleic acids. The complex, helical structure of this macromolecule holds within it a simple coding system, based only on four different chemicals called nucleotides, that instructs the cell how to build the proteins necessary for homeostasis. All cells contain DNA, which is held within the nucleus of eukaryotic cells, and ribosomes, which are the molecular machines needed to construct new proteins.

Ribonucleic acid (RNA) is the only other kind of nucleic acid, but there are various types of RNA that play different roles in gene expression. All organisms make an RNA copy of a gene and use that copy to build protein on the ribosome.

Understanding DNA structure, replication, and its use by the cell is essential for understanding how DNA is passed from cell to cell, how mutations arise, and the consequences of those mutations (from harmless to lethal). The concepts you learn here are also the basis for cloning, genetic modification, gene therapy, and forensic techniques like DNA fingerprinting.

DNA is an abbreviation for the molecule **deoxyribonucleic acid**. The DNA molecule is described as a *double-stranded helix*. Each strand of DNA is a long chain of **nucleotides**, the monomers of nucleic acids. Each nucleotide consists of three chemical components: a **phosphate** group, a 5-carbon **sugar**, and a nitrogen-containing **base**. In DNA, the sugar is *deoxyribose*, which has one less oxygen than *ribose*, the sugar in RNA.

Fig. 14.1 shows the detailed structure of the DNA molecule. Each nucleotide monomer (sugar + phosphate + base) is linked to the next by a bond between the sugar of one nucleotide and the phosphate of the other. This is referred to as the **sugar-phosphate backbone** of each strand. The two strands are held to each other by hydrogen bonds that form between the exposed bases from each nucleotide.

Each DNA nucleotide contains one of four different kinds of bases, abbreviated **A, T, G, and C** (Fig. 14.1). These bases bond with each other in exclusive pairs: A only with T, and G only with C. This is referred to as **complementary base-pairing**. Two hydrogen bonds form between AT pairs, while three hydrogen bonds form between CG pairs. Individually, hydrogen bonds are weak, but because there are so many base pairs in a single DNA molecule (from 50 million to 250 million!) they hold the two strands together tightly.

The single strands of DNA are oriented opposite of each other.

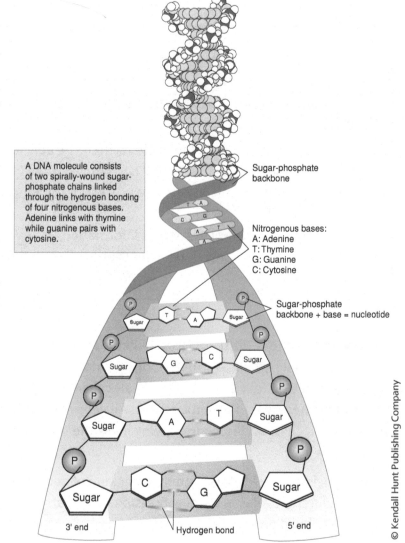

A DNA molecule consists of two spirally-wound sugar-phosphate chains linked through the hydrogen bonding of four nitrogenous bases. Adenine links with thymine while guanine pairs with cytosine.

Sugar-phosphate backbone

Nitrogenous bases:
A: Adenine
T: Thymine
G: Guanine
C: Cytosine

Sugar-phosphate backbone + base = nucleotide

3' end

Hydrogen bond

5' end

Figure 14.1   Structure of the DNA double helix. Repeated nucleotides make up the two strands of DNA, which are joined by complementary base pairs and twist together in a spiral.

One end is the **5′ end**, the other is the **3′ end**. They are described this way because the carbon atoms in the sugar that participate in the bonds between the nucleotides are the 5th and 3rd carbons. This orientation is described as **antiparallel**.

Build a DNA Molecule

Exercise 1

Follow the activities described below using the DNA model kit at your table.

1. Work with the other students to organize the kit pieces into separate piles. Make sure you understand what each piece represents.
2. Build a single nucleotide that can be found in DNA. What three pieces will you need to snap together? _____ _____ _____
3. Which chemical component of each DNA nucleotide can differ between nucleotides? _____
4. Work quickly with your group to construct 12 separate DNA nucleotides, 3 of each base. Then, construct just a single DNA strand that has the following base sequence: CAATGC
5. When you connect one nucleotide to the next to make this single strand, which chemical components of the nucleotides make this connection? _____ _____
6. What will be the complementary base sequence to the strand you built in #4?
   __ __ __ __ __ __
7. Use the remaining nucleotides to build the complementary strand and assemble the DNA molecule.
8. Notice that the pairs of complementary bases fit together but do not "snap" together like when you built the strands. What is being represented by this difference?
9. Look at the portion of DNA you have built and check your understanding by answering the following questions:

   - Can you identify a single nucleotide?
   - Do you know what is meant by a sugar-phosphate backbone?
   - Do you understand why DNA is described as "double-stranded"?
   - Can you identify a complementary base-pair?
   - Do you know which components are connected by covalent bonds, and which ones are connected by hydrogen bonds?

14.2 DNA REPLICATION

A **chromosome** is DNA wrapped around protein for support and structure. Human cells contain 46 chromosomes. When a cell divides, the resulting daughter cells must also have 46 chromosomes in their nuclei, meaning that the original parent cell must undergo **DNA replication** to make a complete copy of all its chromosomes prior to cell division during the S phase of interphase.

DNA replication is an intricate process carried out by several different enzymes working together (Fig. 14.2). Two of these enzymes are important to know. **Helicase** unwinds the two DNA strands by breaking the hydrogen bonds between complementary base pairs. Each of the original separated strands now serves as a template for the construction of a new complementary strand. **DNA polymerase** is the enzyme that positions free nucleotides according to their complementarity to the template strand and joins these new nucleotides together (sugar-to-phosphate) with covalent bonds to form the new strand in the 5′ to 3′ direction. Due to the anti-parallel nature of DNA, this makes one strand the **leading strand**

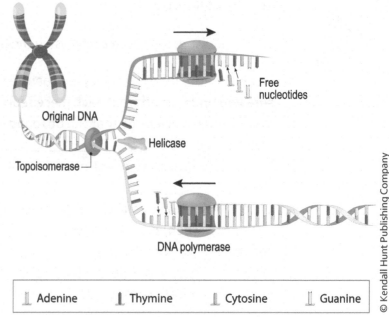

| ⫿ Adenine | ⫿ Thymine | ⫿ Cytosine | ⫿ Guanine |

Figure 14.2   DNA Replication. DNA replication is semiconservative—each of the original strands is used as a template for the creation of a new complementary strand.

that builds continuously, and a **lagging strand** that builds discontinuously. The process is **semiconservative**, meaning each new DNA molecule consists of one original strand and one newly-made strand.

Exercise 2

Simulate DNA Replication

Use the DNA molecule you made previously and follow the procedures below to conduct DNA replication.

1. Simulate unwinding by the _____ enzyme by separating the two DNA strands.

2. Each original strand serves as a template for base-pairing by _____ (which enzyme?). Construct new complementary strands for each template to create two new DNA molecules.

3. Look at the two new DNA molecules and check your understanding by answering these questions:

   - Are the new DNA molecules identical to each other?
   - Are the new DNA molecules identical to the original DNA molecule?
   - Do you understand why the process is described as semiconservative?
   - Where in the eukaryotic cell does DNA replication occur?
   - It is during DNA replication that most errors in the base sequence of DNA arise. What do we call these types of errors?

Genes provide instructions for cells to build the proteins that give us our traits (e.g., eye color, height, dietary restrictions). Thus, **gene expression** is the creation of functional protein from the information in DNA. Gene expression is a two-step process. **Transcription** take place in the nucleus and creates a strand of messenger RNA (mRNA) from a gene in DNA. The mRNA passes through the nuclear pores to enter the cytoplasm. **Translation** occurs on a ribosome, which facilitates the interaction between mRNA and transfer RNA (tRNA) molecules to join amino acids together to build a protein.

STRUCTURE OF RNA

RNA (ribonucleic acid) is also a nucleic acid composed of nucleotides, but RNA differs from DNA in many ways (Fig. 14.3). RNA is always single-stranded and the sugar in each nucleotide is ribose. Another major structural difference from DNA is that one base, uracil (U), replaces thymine (T), meaning that A and U are complementary.

Three kinds of RNA play a role in gene expression:

- **Messenger RNA (mRNA)** is the product of transcription in the nucleus. It is a copy of the gene in DNA. mRNA holds the codons that identify the amino acid sequence for the protein being built by the ribosome.
- **Transfer RNA (tRNA)** is a molecule that carries an amino acid to the ribosome to add to the growing polypeptide (aka protein). tRNA holds an anticodon that is complementary to the codon on mRNA, ensuring the correct placement of the amino acid.
- **Ribosomal RNA (rRNA)**, along with protein, is part of the structural composition of the ribosome.

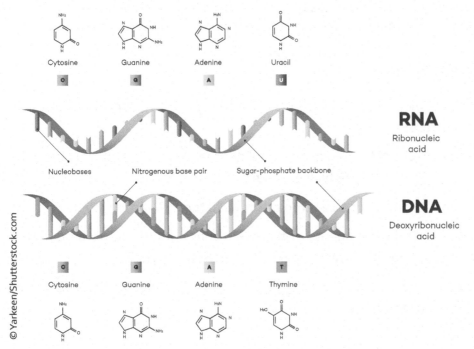

© Yarkeen/Shutterstock.com

Figure 14.3 RNA vs. DNA. RNA is a single-stranded nucleic acid whereas DNA is double-stranded. The nitrogenous base uracil (U) in RNA replaces thymine (T).

TRANSCRIPTION

Transcription begins when the enzyme **RNA polymerase** attaches to the DNA molecule at the gene of interest (remember that we are interested in building one protein from the information in one gene—which is just a limited sequence of bases, a very small portion of the large DNA molecule). RNA polymerase travels along the gene breaking the hydrogen bonds between complementary bases and building mRNA by base-pairing with one of the DNA strands. The DNA molecule is unaffected as it winds back up behind RNA polymerase while the single-stranded mRNA transcript spools outward. When completed, the mRNA transcript exits the nucleus through the nuclear pore (Fig. 14.4).

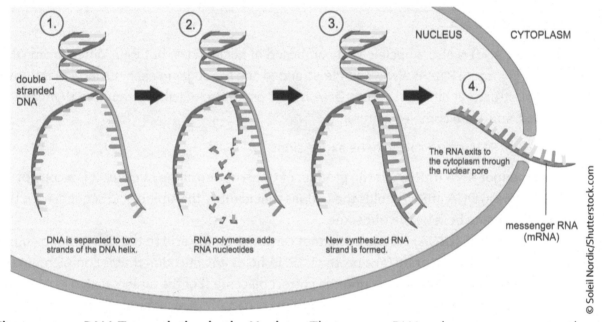

Figure 14.4   DNA Transcription in the Nucleus. The enzyme RNA polymerase separates the DNA strands and base-pairs with one strand to create mRNA which leaves the nucleus. The DNA strands will come back together into helical form until the next time transcription takes place.

Simulate DNA Transcription

Exercise 3

Use one of the DNA molecules you made previously and follow the procedures below to conduct DNA transcription.

1. Separate the two DNA strands to simulate the unwinding of the gene by _____ (which enzyme?).

2. Use one of the DNA strands as a template to build the mRNA transcript.

3. Which two chemical components of the mRNA nucleotides had to be different from DNA nucleotides to correctly make the mRNA transcript?

4. Where did this process take place? _____ Why *must* it occur in this location in the eukaryotic cell?

TRANSLATION

Translation is the process by which a ribosome uses the base sequence of the mRNA transcript to construct a protein. The bases in mRNA are read in groups of three called **codons**. Each codon represents an amino acid, except for some *stop codons* that end the process. Fig. 14.5 is a codon chart that shows all 64 possible codons and the amino acids they represent.

The amino acids are carried individually by tRNA molecules which expose a group of three bases, called the **anticodon**, that are complementary to a specific codon on mRNA. In this way, the sequence of codons originally dictated by the DNA specifies the correct order of amino acids brought by tRNA molecules attracted by the codon-anticodon complementarity.

	Second Base				
First Base	**U**	**C**	**A**	**G**	**Third Base**
U	UUU phenylalanine	UCU serine	UAU tyrosine	UGU cysteine	U
	UUC phenylalanine	UCC serine	UAC tyrosine	UGC cysteine	C
	UUA leucine	UCA serine	UAA stop	UGA stop	A
	UUG leucine	UCG serine	UAG stop	UGG tryptophan	G
C	CUU leucine	CCU proline	CAU histidine	CGU arginine	U
	CUC leucine	CCC proline	CAC histidine	CGC arginine	C
	CUA leucine	CCA proline	CAA glutamine	CGA arginine	A
	CUG leucine	CCG proline	CAG glutamine	CGG arginine	G
A	AUU isoleucine	ACU threonine	AAU asparagine	AGU serine	U
	AUC isoleucine	ACC threonine	AAC asparagine	AGC serine	C
	AUA isoleucine	ACA threonine	AAA lysine	AGA arginine	A
	AUG(start) methionine	ACG threonine	AAG lysine	AGG arginine	G
G	GUU valine	GCU alanine	GAU aspartate	GGU glycine	U
	GUC valine	GCC alanine	GAC aspartate	GGC glycine	C
	GUA valine	GCA alanine	GAA glutamate	GGA glycine	A
	GUG valine	GCG alanine	GAG glutamate	GGG glycine	G

Figure 14.5   Codon chart. The 20 different amino acids needed to build all proteins each have a unique codon. One start codon, AUG, codes for methionine and signals the start of translation, while three others are stop codons that signal the end of translation.

CHECK YOUR UNDERSTANDING

From the information in the codon chart, why might some DNA mutations have no effect on the protein being built?

The ribosome attaches to the mRNA in the cytoplasm and begins to read the base sequence of the transcript. When the ribosome encounters the start codon AUG in its reading frame the process of translation begins. Three major phases of translation are recognized:

1. **Initiation**—The ribosome combines with mRNA and begins reading until a start codon is found and then the first tRNA molecule enters carrying the first amino acid.

2. **Elongation**—Each new tRNA molecule that arrives enters the A site on the ribosome. The tRNA holding the growing chain of amino acids (the protein being built) is in the P site. A *peptide bond* is formed between the amino acid chain and the new amino acid in the A site through *dehydration synthesis*. The tRNA in the P site, no longer holding the protein, exits and the mRNA advances through the ribosome so that the growing protein is again held by a tRNA molecule in the P site. The A site is open and ready to receive the next tRNA carrying the next amino acid (Fig. 14.6). This process repeats as the mRNA is read until a stop codon appears.

3. **Termination**—Once a stop codon appears, a chemical called a release factor binds the A site stimulating the ribosome to release the completed protein.

Understanding Translation

Use the mRNA molecule you previously created and follow the procedures below to learn about translation on the ribosome.

Exercise 4

1. Look at the mRNA transcript you made in Exercise 3. How many codons appear on your mRNA? ___ How many tRNA molecules will interact with this small portion of mRNA? ___

2. Use the model kit to build the tRNA molecules that will interact with your mRNA. You will need to attach an amino acid to each tRNA you build.

3. Guide one tRNA to the mRNA and match the anticodon to the codon. Bring the next tRNA to the next codon and join the amino acids together. Be sure to simulate dehydration synthesis, which creates the by-product water, H_2O.

4. Fig. 14.6 shows the elongation phase of translation. Make your own labels on Fig. 14.6 using these terms: **amino acid, tRNA, P site, A site, ribosome, mRNA, codon, anticodon, peptide bond.**

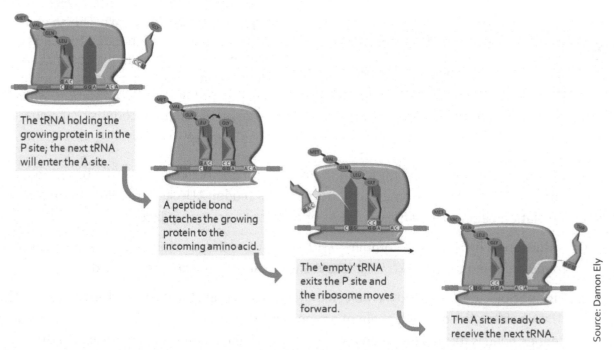

The tRNA holding the growing protein is in the P site; the next tRNA will enter the A site.

A peptide bond attaches the growing protein to the incoming amino acid.

The 'empty' tRNA exits the P site and the ribosome moves forward.

The A site is ready to receive the next tRNA.

Source: Damon Ely

Figure 14.6 Elongation Phase of Protein Synthesis. Following initiation, tRNA molecules deliver amino acids one at a time by matching their anticodons with the codons on mRNA. The ribosome facilitates this interaction as it 'reads' the mRNA.

REVIEW QUESTIONS

1. Name the three chemical components of a nucleotide.

2. Which kind of bonds, ionic, covalent, or hydrogen, hold together the sugar-phosphate backbone?

3. Which kind of bonds, ionic, covalent, or hydrogen, hold together the two strands of DNA?

4. Why do cells replicate their DNA? Explain.

5. During replication the two strands of DNA are separated from each other. Each strand is now a *template* strand. Why are they called templates?

6. Which enzyme unwinds the two DNA strands? Which enzyme builds the new strand?

7. Fill in the blanks: When you smell delicious food, nervous impulses are sent to your salivary glands to increase production of saliva. The cells of the salivary glands will need to make the enzyme, *salivary* _____, to break down starch in the food you are about to eat. To begin making this protein, an enzyme named _____ will find the correct gene and build the mRNA molecule in a process known as _____. The mRNA will leave the nucleus and combine with a large _____ in the cytoplasm, where the protein will be constructed in a process called _____. The cell will then secrete the newly-made enzyme into the saliva mixture.

8. On which molecule would you find the *codon*: DNA, mRNA, tRNA, or rRNA? On which would you find the *anticodon*?

9. Suppose you know the base sequence of a gene and you want to know which amino acids will result from a portion of the DNA strand with the following base sequence: TAC CCA

If RNA polymerase transcribes this portion of the DNA strand, what would be the complementary base sequence of the mRNA transcript? __ __ __ __ __ __

Find these two codons in the codon chart in Figure 14.5 to identify the amino acids. Write down their names. _____ _____

10. Most mutations arise during DNA replication. If the daughter cells receiving the mutated DNA are egg or sperm cells, there is a possibility of passing the mutation on to offspring. Explain how it would be possible for a mutation that alters only a single base could result in a disease because of a malfunctioning protein.

CHAPTER 15
MITOSIS

 ## Laboratory Objectives

By the end of this laboratory, the student should be able to:

- understand the cell cycle and its subdivisions;
- describe the chromosomal events that occur during mitosis;
- distinguish between plant and animal cytokinesis;
- understand why mitotic divisions are necessary in living systems.

Cell division is central to the life of all organisms. All cells come from pre-existing cells as a result of cell division. Newly created cells are subject to wear and tear, as well as accidents in our universe that favor disorder, and they are, therefore, bound to die. If a multicellular organism is to continue to live, it must create new cells at a rate as fast as that at which its cells die. For example, in adult humans millions of cells must divide every second simply to maintain the status quo.

Eukaryotic cells may experience two types of cell division: mitotic cell division and meiotic cell division. This exercise deals with mitotic cell division. Meiotic cell division will be considered in the following lab exercise. Prokaryotic cells divide by binary fission. They do not divide by either mitotic or meiotic cell division.

Mitotic cell division consists of two sequential processes: nuclear division (called **mitosis**) and cytoplasmic division (called **cytokinesis**). Mitotic cell division produces daughter cells that are genetically identical to each other and also genetically identical to the cell which divided to give rise to them.

During most of its lifetime, a given cell is not dividing. All cells have what is called a **cell cycle**, and the cell division phase accounts for only a small fraction of the total cell cycle. The phase of the cell cycle when a cell is not dividing is denoted as **interphase**. A typical cell cycle for eukaryotic cells is presented on the following page.

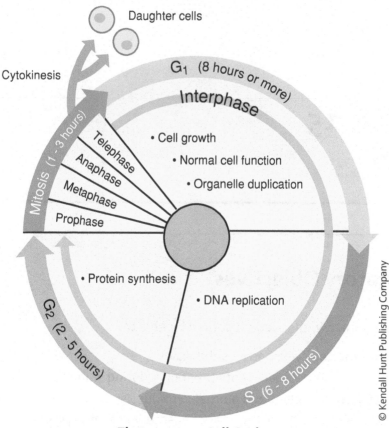

Figure 15.1   Cell Cycle.

M = M phase = period of mitosis and cytokinesis.

G_1 = First gap phase = interval between the end of mitotic cell division and the start of DNA synthesis. (Regulation of the length of the cell cycle occurs primarily by arresting at a specific point of G_1. Therefore, this phase has the most variable length.)

S = S phase = specific part of interphase during which DNA synthesis occurs. (By the end of this phase, each chromosome consists of two identical chromatids.)

G_2 = Second gap phase = interval between the end of DNA synthesis and the start of mitosis. G_0 = A temporary or permanent exit from the cell cycle.

(Cells often pause in G_1 before DNA replication and enter this state [G_0], where they may remain for days to years. Some cells never reenter the cell cycle. At any one time, most of the cells of a multicellular organism are in the G_0 phase.)

G_1, S, and G_2 are subdivisions of the portion of the cell cycle referred to as **interphase**. Interphase normally comprises 90% or more of the total cell cycle time.

The M phase of the cell cycle begins with mitosis and ends with cytokinesis. Mitosis is subdivided into four phases: prophase, metaphase, anaphase, and telophase.

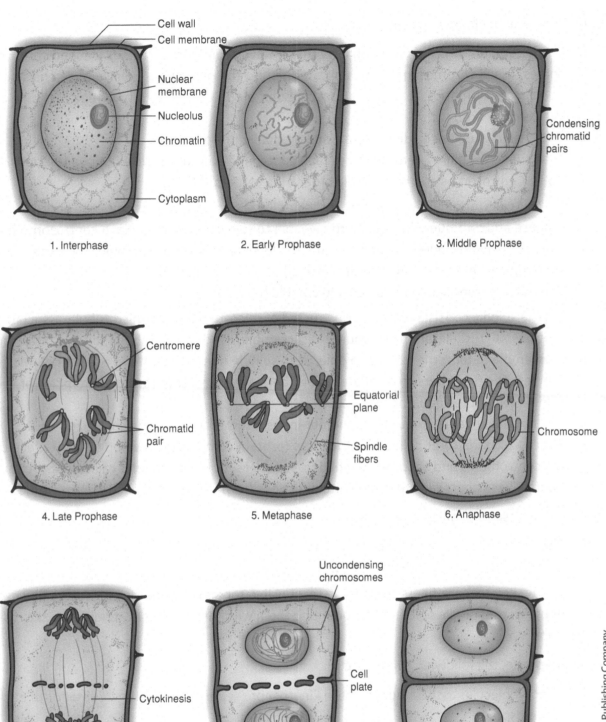

Figure 15.2   Mitosis in Plant Cells.

1. Interphase

Cell wall
Cell membrane
Nuclear membrane
Nucleolus
Chromatin
Cytoplasm

2. Early Prophase

3. Middle Prophase

Condensing chromatid pairs

4. Late Prophase

Centromere
Chromatid pair

5. Metaphase

Equatorial plane
Spindle fibers

6. Anaphase

Chromosome

7. Early Telophase

Cytokinesis

8. Late Telophase

Uncondensing chromosomes
Cell plate

9. Daughter Cells

During **prophase** the following events occur:

1. The chromatin, which is diffuse in interphase, slowly condenses into well-defined chromo-somes. (Each chromosome has duplicated during the preceding S phase and consists of two sister chromatids, joined at a specific point along their length by a region known as the **centromere**.)
2. The nucleolus begins to disassemble and gradually disappears.
3. In animal cells, paired centrosomes (each containing paired centrioles) move to opposite poles. Centrosomes are microtubule organizing centers (MTOC).

    (The cell's original centrosome replicates by a process that begins just prior to the S phase and continues through G_2 to give rise to two centrosomes. Each centrosome has a group of microtubules radiating from it. Collectively, these microtubules form the aster. Higher plant cells lack centrioles and asters.)
4. The **mitotic spindle** begins to develop outside the nucleus.

    (The spindle consists of fibers constructed of microtubules and microtubule-associated proteins. Cytoskeletal microtubules disassemble, and their tubulin dimers start to reassemble to form the mitotic spindle. Each spindle fiber is, therefore, a cluster of micro-tubules. The first fibers to form are **polar fibers**, which extend from the two poles of the spindle toward the equator of the cell.)
5. The nuclear envelope breaks into membranous fragments indistinguishable from ER.
6. Specialized structures called **kinetochores** (protein complexes) develop on either face of the centromeres and become attached to a special set of microtubules called **kinetochore fibers**. These fibers radiate in opposite directions from each side of each chromosome.

During **metaphase**, the following events occur:

1. The chromosomes become arranged so that their centromeres all lie in one plane (the **Metaphase plate**) near the middle of the cell.

    (The kinetochore fibers seem to be responsible for aligning the chromosomes halfway between the spindle poles and for orienting them with their long axes at right angles to the spindle axis.)

During **anaphase**, the following events occur:

1. Motor molecules associated with each kinetochore separate the sister chromatids of each chromosome.
2. Each chromatid (now called a chromosome) is moved slowly toward a spindle pole by the motor molecules of the kinetochore as they "walk" along the kinetochore microtubules.
3. Kinetochore fibers (microtubules) progressively shorten (by depolymerizing at their kine-tochore ends) as the chromosomes approach the poles.
4. Polar fibers (microtubules) elongate and move the two poles of the spindle further apart.

These non-kinetochore microtubules elongate the whole cell along the polar axis. During **telophase**, the following events occur:

1. As the separated chromosomes (formerly called sister chromatids) arrive at the poles, the kinetochore fibers disappear.
2. A new nuclear envelope reforms around each group of chromosomes.
3. The condensed chromatin disperses once more.
4. Nucleoli reappear.

In animal cells, cytokinesis is accomplished by the development of a **cleavage furrow**. The cleavage furrow forms as a result of the interaction of actin and myosin filaments, which form a contractile ring just below the plasma membrane. In plant cells, cytokinesis is accomplished by the formation of a **cell plate**, rather than a cleavage furrow. The cell plate is assembled as Golgi-derived vesicles containing cell wall material are directed to the center of the dividing cell by microtubules. The vesicles then fuse with each other to create the cell plate.

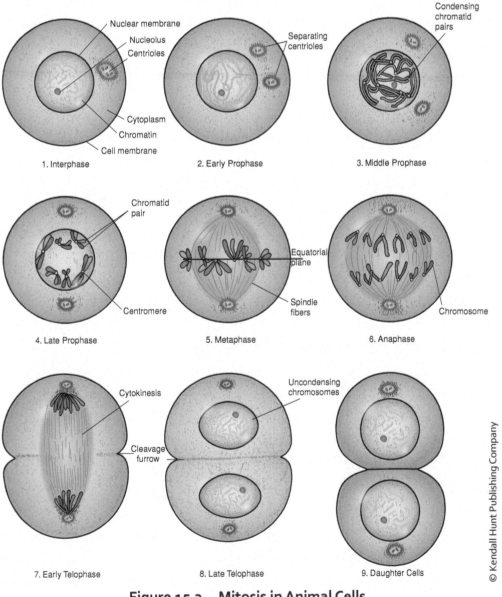

Figure 15.3   Mitosis in Animal Cells.

MATERIALS

Prepared slides—onion root tip, whitefish blastula

Microscope

Exercise 1

Onion Root Tip Mitosis

Obtain a prepared slide of an onion (**Allium**) root tip. Focus on the slide so that you are viewing an area just above the tip. Do not focus on the very tip because these are protective root cap cells and are not undergoing mitosis. Switch to the 40X objective and observe individual cells.

1. Locate a cell in **interphase**. Sketch this cell and label the nuclear envelope, nucleolus, and cell wall.

Do you see any visible indication that this cell is preparing to divide?

If so, what indication?

2. Locate a cell in **prophase**. Can you distinguish the chromosomes?

Is a distinct nuclear envelope obvious?

Sketch this prophase cell, indicate the direction of the spindle fibers, and label the chromosomes, centromeres, and poles.

3. Locate a cell in **metaphase**. How can the metaphase cell be distinguished from prophase?

Sketch the metaphase cell and label the chromosomes, spindle fibers, and poles.

4. Locate a cell in **anaphase**. What is the major event of anaphase?

Are two groups of chromosomes visible?

Sketch and label the anaphase cell.

5. Locate a cell in **telophase**. Is the cell plate visible?

Has the nucleus reformed?

Sketch and label the telophase cell.

6. If onions have a chromosome number of 16, how many chromosomes are in each of the daughter cells formed by cytokinesis at the end of telophase?_____ How many chromosomes were in the original cell?_____

Exercise
2

Whitefish Mitosis

Obtain a slide labeled **whitefish blastula** to study mitotic cell division in an animal. The blastula is a stage of embryonic development. When a sperm fertilizes an egg cell, a zygote is produced. This zygote divides by mitotic cell division to produce a ball of cells known as a blastula. Mitotic cell divisions will be one of the major events that will allow this early embryonic stage to grow and develop into an adult organism.

Focus on the whitefish slide and switch to the 40× objective. Locate and examine a cell in each phase of mitosis. You might want to make a sketch of each phase.

If the chromosome number of the whitefish cell were 24, how many chromosomes would be in each daughter cell?_____.

Indicate three places in your body where there is a high rate of mitotic cell division.

1. _____

2. _____

3. _____

Exercise 3

Models of Mitotic Cell Division

A series of models that shows mitotic cell division as it occurs in animal cells is available in the laboratory. Study these so that you understand what is being represented by each model.

Exercise 4

Estimate the Time Spent in Each Phase of Mitosis

If a phase of mitosis takes longer than others, it should appear more often in a specimen. We can use the frequency with which each phase of mitosis appears in the onion root tip to estimate the time spent in each phase. Obtain an Onion Root Tip slide and focus on a section near the tip under the high-power objective lens (40X) and follow the procedure below.

- Begin to move systematically up and down columns of cells and make a tally mark in the appropriate column of Table 15.1 for each cell you encounter that is in one of the four phases of mitosis until you have a grand total of 30 tally marks.

Table 15.1   Tally of onion root tip cells in different phases of mitosis.

Mitotic Phase	Tally Marks	Sum
Prophase		
Metaphase		
Anaphase		
Telophase		
		Total = 30

- The average duration of mitosis in the onion root tip is 90 minutes. You can estimate the time spent in a mitotic phase by multiplying the proportion of cells that were found in that phase by 90 minutes.
- Complete Table 15.2 to estimate the time spent in each phase.

Table 15.2   Calculation of time spent in each phase of mitosis.

Mitotic Phase	Proportion of Total (# cells observed / 30)	Time Spent in Mitotic Phase (proportion × 90 minutes)
Prophase		
Metaphase		
Anaphase		
Telophase		

?

1. Which phase of mitosis appears to take the most amount of time?

    interphase

2. Considering what you know about the events during each phase, why do you think this phase needs the most time? Explain.

    organization of DNA and the replication of

    chromosomes makes the process longer

3. What are some possible sources of error in your investigation? What would you do differently next time?

4. Why might a cancer researcher conduct an investigation like this? How could they use the information gained?

PRACTICE QUESTIONS

?

1. _chromosome_ a complex of DNA and protein housed in the nucleus of the cell.

2. _anaphase_ the stage of mitosis where sister chromatids separate, moving to opposite poles.

3. _cytokinesis_ refers to the division of the cytoplasm and associated organelles.

4. _telephase_ the last stage of the mitotic process where spindle fibers dissipate.

5. _~~interphase~~ S phase_ preparatory event to mitosis where DNA replicates.

6. _mitosis_ refers to division of the nuclear material.

7. _DNA_ the genetic material housed in the chromosomes.

8. _~~cell mitosis~~ cellular reproduction_ the entire process whereby cells reproduce themselves (two words).

9. _metaphase_ the stage of mitosis where chromatid pairs align at the cell equatorial plane.

10. _prophase_ the first stage of mitosis where chromosomes become observable.

11. _centrioles_ cytoplasmic organelles that help produce spindle fibers.

12. _centromere_ attachment site of spindle fibers on the chromatids.

13. _DNA replication_ process whereby DNA reproduces itself.

CHAPTER 16
MEIOSIS

 Laboratory Objectives

By the end of this laboratory, the student should be able to:

- explain the relevance of meiosis to sexual reproduction;
- understand the difference between haploid and diploid cells;
- describe homologous chromosomes and how they differ from sister chromatids;
- describe the events of meiosis;
- list the differences between mitosis and meiosis.

Meiosis is two rounds of nuclear division that results in the creation of **gametes** (i.e., **egg** and **sperm**) within the **gonads** (i.e., **ovaries** and **testes**) of animals. Many of the events of meiosis are like mitosis; however, the most important difference is that meiosis creates cells that are **haploid (n)**, meaning they possess only <u>one</u> full set of chromosomes. **Diploid (2n)** cells (which are most of the cells in your body) possess <u>two</u> full sets of chromosomes—one set inherited from each parent. Both meiosis and mitosis begin with a diploid cell, but the daughter cells created through mitosis remain diploid while the daughter cells of meiosis are haploid. For this reason, meiosis is called "reduction division"—the total number of chromosomes is reduced by half.

Sexual reproduction involves the fertilization of an egg cell (n) by a sperm cell (n) to create a **zygote** (2n) that goes on to become an **embryo**. These events occur in both plants and animals. Humans have 23 unique chromosomes that contain all the necessary genes; these 23 chromosomes constitute one "set". Thus, diploid cells possess two sets, or two of each chromosome, for a total of 46 chromosomes. The pairs of chromosomes, one from each parent, are called **homologous chromosomes**—they have the same genes in the same locations (although the genes can have different forms known as *alleles*). Unlike mitosis, meiosis separates homologous chromosomes into different daughter cells, cutting the chromosome number in half.

In this laboratory you will become familiar with the events of meiosis and the ways in which it differs from mitosis. Understanding meiosis is an important step towards learning about patterns of inheritance and the underlying causes of the genetic variation we observe in organisms.

16.1 HOMOLOGOUS CHROMOSOMES AND SISTER CHROMATIDS

Most of the cells of your body are diploid with pairs of homologous chromosomes present in the nucleus and are known as somatic cells. Each unique chromosome differs in size, holds different genes, and is numbered except for the 23rd pair of sex chromosomes, which are known as X and Y. Thus, your diploid cells possess two each of chromosome 1, chromosome 2, and so on. We often illustrate homologous chromosomes with different colors indicating their maternal and paternal origins (Fig. 16.1).

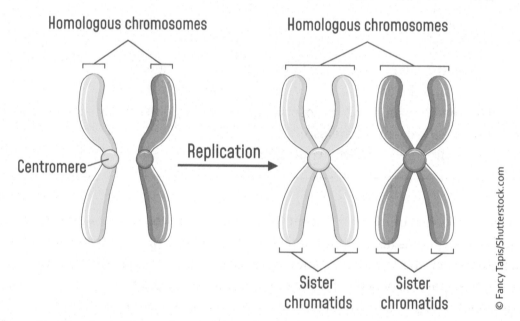

Figure 16.1   Replication of homologous chromosomes. Homologous chromosomes from each parent (indicated by differing colors) are replicated to produce sister chromatids joined by a centromere.

Prior to either meiosis or mitosis, each chromosome is replicated during the S phase of interphase. DNA replication results in identical **sister chromatids** attached by a bundle of proteins known as the **centromere** (Fig. 16.1). Sister chromatids are identical copies because they are the products of replication; homologous chromosomes possess the same genes, but they are not necessarily identical because the **alleles**, or forms of those genes, can differ. For example, two homologous chromosomes in a plant cell will both have the gene for petal color, but one chromosome may possess the allele for purple petals while the other chromosome's allele may code for white petals.

Build Homologous Chromosomes

Follow the activities described below using the chromosome kit at your table.

Exercise 1

1. Observe the contents of your kit. The red and yellow plastic beads attach to each other to create chromosomes of various sizes. The red and yellow magnetic pieces represent centromeres.

2. As a group, construct a pair of homologous chromosomes as they would appear during the G1 phase of interphase (prior to replication).

3. Now, replicate each chromosome to create two homologous chromosomes that each consist of a pair of sister chromatids.

4. Work quickly with your group to construct a second pair of homologous chromosomes that have replicated. Remember that this pair is a different chromosome than the first pair, and this difference should be reflected in the overall size of the chromosomes.

5. Have your instructor check your chromosomes when you are finished and then draw the chromosomes in the space below. You will continue to use these models in the activities that follow.

16.2 EVENTS OF MEIOSIS

Meiosis is two rounds of nuclear division, resulting in a total of four haploid daughter cells (gametes). This type of cell division occurs to produce **germ** cells. Each round of division, known as **meiosis I** and **meiosis II**, progresses through prophase, metaphase, anaphase, and telophase stages as you previously learned. We must be specific about the timing of events, so we recognize each phase individually as belonging to either meiosis I or II (e.g., "prophase I", "anaphase II", etc.). Fig.16.2 shows the sequence of events during meiosis.

MEIOSIS I: SEPARATION OF HOMOLOGOUS CHROMOSOMES

The first round of nuclear division shuffles some of the genes between each pair of homologous chromosomes and then pulls them apart, placing them into different daughter cells. Many of the events of each phase are like mitosis, such as the degradation and return of the nucleus, and the formation and disintegration of the spindle. It is the behavior of the chromosomes during some phases of meiosis that differs greatly from mitosis. We will explore these specific moments in more detail.

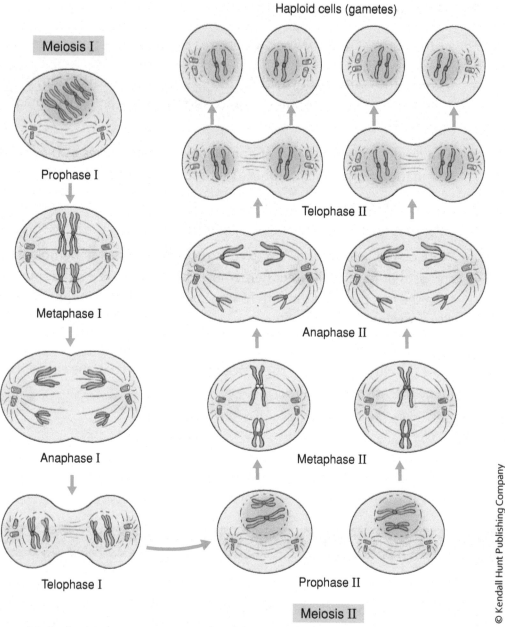

Figure 16.2 Meiosis. Meiosis is two rounds of division resulting in the creation of four haploid daughter cells.

PROPHASE I

During prophase I, the fully-replicated chromosomes, known as **dyads**, condense into their chromatid form as in prophase of mitosis. However, homologous chromosomes pair up during prophase I and fuse together, a process called **synapsis**, to form a single **tetrad**. During this time, some pieces of DNA are swapped between the nonsister chromatids within the tetrad—an event known as **crossing-over** (Figure 16.3).

Crossing-Over and Recombination

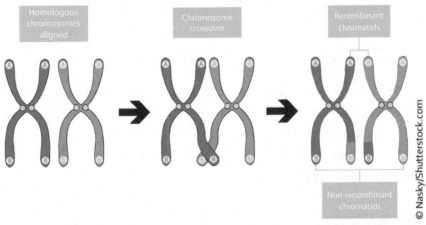

Figure 16.3   Crossing-over. Nonsister chromatids swap genes during prophase I, causing each chromatid to possess a unique combination of alleles.

Crossing-over is a powerful mechanism to create genetic variation because it results in the **recombination** of alleles in each chromatid (i.e., each chromatid possesses a unique combination of alleles that will potentially be inherited by the offspring). Crossing-over contributes to the differences in traits we observe between siblings despite their origin from the same two parents.

Simulate Prophase I

Exercise 2

Use the homologous chromosomes you previously made to simulate synapsis and crossing-over. Sketch the final appearance of your chromosomes in the space to the right.

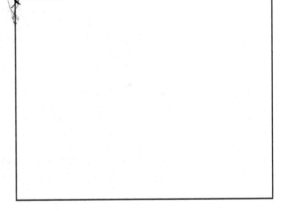

METAPHASE I

In metaphase I, the nucleus has completely disappeared, the spindle is fully extended across the cell, and the pairs of homologous chromosomes are aligned along the spindle equator (Fig. 16.2). The homologous chromosomes align in this paired way in preparation for their separation. Each pair arranges itself in a side-by-side fashion randomly, without regard to the maternal or paternal origin of the chromosome. This is called **independent assortment** and it is the second major source of genetic variation created in offspring.

Looking at metaphase I in Fig. 16.2, the two pairs of homologous chromosomes are oriented in different ways. They could just as easily have oriented in the same way—it is completely random and the orientation (i.e., the assortment) of one pair has no effect (i.e., it is independent) on the orientation of the next pair. Each gamete produced will thus contain chromosomes from both of that individual's parents. Considering the swapping of individual genes during crossing-over, the chances of any two gametes being identical is exceedingly small.

ANAPHASE I + TELOPHASE I

In anaphase I, the nucleus remains absent and the spindle fibers begin to retract as each homologous chromosome is pulled to the opposite side of the cell (Fig. 16.2). Notice that the sister chromatids remain connected by the centromere. During telophase I, new nuclei will begin to form around each cluster of loosening chromosomes as the spindle disappears, and cytokinesis begins to form a cleavage furrow (Fig. 16.2).

Exercise 3

Complete Meiosis I

Simulate metaphase I, anaphase I, and telophase I using the homologous chromosomes you previously constructed.

1. Sketch the contents of each of the two daughter cells in the space to the right.

2. How many chromosomes were in the original parent cell you created in exercise 1?

3. How many chromosomes are in each of the daughter cells you just created?

4. Are the daughter cells you created haploid (n) or diploid (2n)?

MEIOSIS II: SEPARATION OF SISTER CHROMATIDS

After a short period of time called *interkinesis*, meiosis II begins in each of the daughter cells created at the end of meiosis I. The phases of meiosis II are identical to mitosis; the only difference is that each cell contains half the number of chromosomes. Fig. 16.2 shows how the chromosomes condense during prophase II, they line up along the spindle equator during metaphase II, the sister chromatids are separated during anaphase II, and the new nuclei form during telophase II as cytokinesis begins.

Complete Meiosis II

Simulate prophase II, metaphase II, anaphase II, and telophase II using the homologous chromosomes you previously constructed.

1. Sketch the contents of each of the four daughter cells in the space below.

2. How many chromosomes are in each of the daughter cells you just created? Compare the ploidy (whether it is haploid or diploid) of the daughter cells after meiosis I to the ploidy of the daughter cells after meiosis II. Are they different? Explain. Two - they diploid

3. Are any of the four daughter cells genetically identical? Why or why not?

    NO - Need for genetic variability
    crossing-over

4. Observe the results of other groups in the laboratory; specifically, notice the distribution of maternal and paternal chromosomes in the daughter cells. In this regard, why do some groups have different outcomes than yours?

REVIEW QUESTIONS

1. Complete the following table:

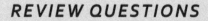

	Mitosis	Meiosis
# of divisions	One	two
# of daughter cells	Two	4
Ploidy of daughter cells	identical	Not
Location in body	somatic	gametes
Daughter cells identical?		
Separation of homologous chromosomes?	NO	Yes
Purpose of process	growth repair	reproduction

2. If you were to look at a drawing of the chromosomes within a nucleus, what would you look for to tell if the cell was diploid (2n)? Explain using the terminology.

look for 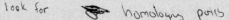 homologous pairs

3. Suppose an organism has a diploid number of 2n = 4 chromosomes. Draw the correct appearance and organization of these four chromosomes during <u>metaphase of mitosis</u> and <u>metaphase I of meiosis</u>.

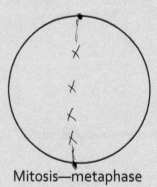

Mitosis—metaphase

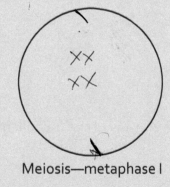

Meiosis—metaphase I

Draw the appearance of the chromosomes inside the nucleus of a single gamete produced from this cell.

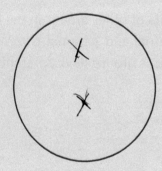

CHAPTER 17
REPRODUCTION AND EARLY EMBRYONIC DEVELOPMENT

 Laboratory Objectives

By the end of this laboratory, the student should be able to:

- identify reproductive system structures of both female and male anatomy;
- describe the functions of female and male reproductive structures;
- describe the processes of spermatogenesis, oogenesis, ovulation, and fertilization;
- list the sequence of events in embryonic development and explain their significance;
- identify the three germ layers and the embryonic structures that arise during neurulation.

The human reproductive system consists of the **gonads** (**ovaries** and **testes**), which produce both **gametes** (**egg** and **sperm**) and **sex hormones** (female: *estrogen* and *progesterone*; male: *testosterone*), and the various accessory organs that either facilitate the release of the gametes (e.g. the ejaculatory duct in males) or provide protection and nourishment for the developing embryo (e.g. the uterus in females). The process of **gametogenesis**, the production of gametes, involves specialized cells undergoing meiosis, but the timing and products differ between females and males.

Following fertilization, the resulting zygote proceeds through five stages of embryonic development within the female reproductive system: **cleavage**, **morula**, **blastocyst**, **gastrula** and **neurula**. Each of these stages are marked by critical events necessary for the proper development of the embryo. Despite the many obvious differences that exist among humans, birds, reptiles and amphibians, there are remarkable similarities in these early embryonic stages that serve as strong evidence for the shared ancestry of vertebrates.

This laboratory will help familiarize you with the major structures and functions of the human reproductive systems and the important developmental stages through which the early embryo passes before most of the major organs have formed, marking the beginning of fetal development.

The role of the male reproductive system is to create sperm cells, a process called **spermatogenesis**, and to deliver these cells to the female reproductive tract. Sperm are produced within the *testes*, which reside in the scrotum. From there, sperm travel through the *epididymis*, *vas deferens*, *ejaculatory duct*, and *urethra* to exit the tip of the *penis* (Fig. 17.1). Along this journey, the *seminal vesicles*, the *prostate gland*, and the *bulbourethral glands* secrete substances that nourish and protect the sperm. The resulting mixture of sperm and glandular secretions is called *semen*.

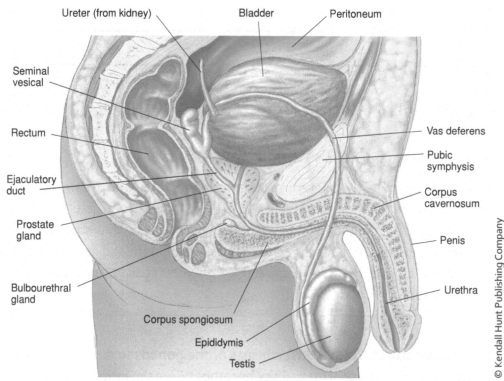

Figure 17.1   Male reproductive system.

Learn the Anatomy of the Male Reproductive System

Find the model of the male reproductive system on display in the lab. Use Fig. 17.1 to help you visually identify the various anatomical structures mentioned in the text above.

Exercise 1

SPERMATOGENESIS

Sperm are produced within the paired oval **testes** held in a sac of skin called the **scrotum**, which resides outside of the abdominal cavity at the base of the penis (Fig. 17.1). This location provides the optimal temperature for maximal sperm production, which is roughly 3°C (5.4°F) lower than the average core body temperature of 37°C (98.6°F).

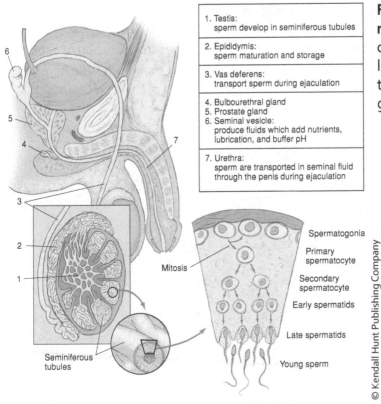

1. Testis: sperm develop in seminiferous tubules
2. Epididymis: sperm maturation and storage
3. Vas deferens: transport sperm during ejaculation
4. Bulbourethral gland 5. Prostate gland 6. Seminal vesicle: produce fluids which add nutrients, lubrication, and buffer pH
7. Urethra: sperm are transported in seminal fluid through the penis during ejaculation

Figure 17.2 Seminiferous tubules reside within the testes. Hundreds of tubules are coiled within separate lobules of each testis. Inside these tubules lie the spermatogonia, which give rise to sperm cells.

© Kendall Hunt Publishing Company

Inside the testes are hundreds of coiled **seminiferous tubules** containing the **spermatogonia**, the cells that will divide to eventually form sperm (Fig. 17.2). Spermatogonia are located at the periphery of the seminiferous tubules where they undergo mitosis to create two diploid (2n) daughter cells: one replacement spermatogonium cell, and one **primary spermatocyte**.

With each cellular division, the daughter cells advance towards the open center (the *lumen*) of the seminiferous tubule. The primary spermatocytes undergo meiosis I to give rise to haploid (n) **secondary spermatocytes**, which then divide via meiosis II to create **spermatids,** or immature sperm. Fig. 17.3 provides an overview of these events.

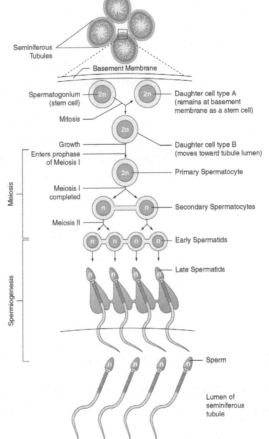

© Kendall Hunt Publishing Company

Figure 17.3 Spermatogenesis. Diploid spermatogonia produce primary spermatocytes via mitosis. These cells then go through meiosis to create immature spermatids.

View Seminiferous Tubules Under the Microscope

Locate the microscope on display in the laboratory showing a cross-section of seminiferous tubules like Fig. 17.4 below. View under low-power first, then under the high-power lens.

Exercise 2

1. Observe the larger, darker spermatogonia around the periphery of each tubule.
2. Observe the smaller, lighter cells below the spermatogonia. These are the primary and secondary spermatocytes.
3. Find the many spermatids that occupy the lumen. Their nuclei appear slender and pointed, and they have long flagella.

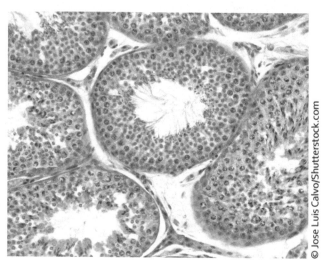

© Jose Luis Calvo/Shutterstock.com

Figure 17.4   Cross-section of seminiferous tubules.

REVIEW QUESTIONS

1. Males can potentially make millions of spermatids each day for their entire life. After learning about the steps of spermatogenesis, how is it possible that males can seemingly make an unlimited amount of sperm cells?

2. During spermatogenesis, which cell is the first to undergo a meiotic division?

3. What is the first haploid cell to be created during spermatogenesis?

THE MALE DUCT SYSTEM

Following their creation in the seminiferous tubules, sperm pass through a series of **accessory ducts**: the epididymis, the vas deferens, the ejaculatory duct, and the urethra.

The **epididymis** surrounds a portion of the testis and is the site of sperm maturation (Fig. 17.1). To become a mature sperm cell capable of successfully fertilizing the female egg, it must shed excess cytoplasm and develop the following three regions (Fig. 17.5):

- **Head**: the cell must flatten the nucleus and produce and store digestive enzymes within a capsule called the **acrosome**.
- **Midpiece**: to provide ATP energy for the whipping flagellum, sperm cells must produce numerous mitochondria that pack tightly around the base of the tail.

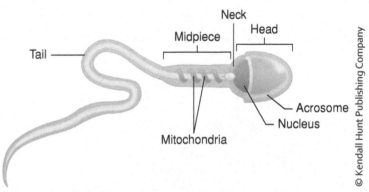

Figure 17.5   A mature sperm cell.

© Kendall Hunt Publishing Company

- **Tail**: the developing sperm must extend the protein fibers that lengthen and whip the flagellum.

Upon sexual stimulation, sperm are ejaculated from the epididymis by the contraction of smooth muscle, moving them next into the vas deferens. The **vas deferens** is a long (45 cm, or 18 inches) tubular duct that extends into the pelvic cavity, loops over the ureter, and joins with the opening of the seminal vesicle to form the short **ejaculatory duct**. The ejaculatory duct enters the prostate gland to merge with the urethra, which passes by the small bulbourethral glands before exiting the penis (Fig. 17.1).

Collectively, the **seminal vesicles**, the **prostate gland**, and the **bulbourethral glands** constitute the *accessory glands* of the male reproductive system (Fig. 17.1). The seminal vesicles provide, among other substances, an abundance of fructose sugar to nourish the sperm. The secretions of these glands make up nearly 70% of semen volume. The prostate is a large gland that produces an activation factor—a chemical that enhances the activity and motility of sperm. Mucus secretions of the bulbourethral glands enter the urethra prior to ejaculation, lubricating the passageway and neutralizing any acidic urine that may be present.

> **REVIEW QUESTIONS**
>
> 1. Sperm are among the most highly specialized cell types. Describe the ways in which the function of a sperm cell is reflected in its form.
>
> 2. Research the surgical procedure known as a vasectomy. Why is it nearly 100% effective in preventing pregnancy?

The role of the female reproductive system is to create egg cells, or *ova*, a process called **oogenesis**, to facilitate fertilization, and to nourish and protect the developing embryo (and later, the fetus). In contrast with males, typically only one immature egg, or *ovum*, develops at a time within one of the paired *ovaries*, which alternate egg production on a 28-day cycle.

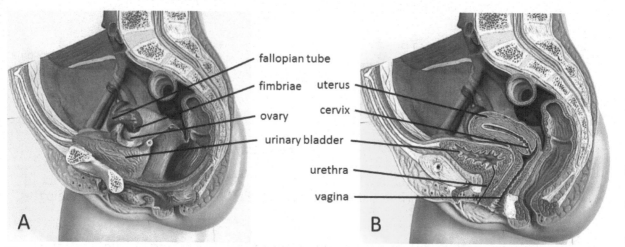

Figure 17.6 The female reproductive system. Panel A: external structure of the urinary bladder; the ovary surrounded by the fimbriae of the fallopian tube. Panel B: sagittal section showing internal structure of the uterus, vagina, and urinary bladder.

The ovum is released from the ovary and is swept into the *oviduct*, or *fallopian tube*, by long extensions called *fimbriae* (Fig. 17.6). Should copulation occur at this time, the egg may be fertilized by a sperm cell to create a single-celled diploid (2n) *zygote* that will begin to divide as it passes through the oviduct and enters the *uterus*, where it will implant into the uterine wall.

The uterus extends toward the *vagina* by a narrow constriction called the *cervix*. In contrast to the male system, the urinary system (urinary bladder and urethra) is separate from the female reproductive system (Fig. 17.6).

Learn the Anatomy of the Female Reproductive System

Find the model of the female reproductive system on display in the lab. Use Fig. 17.6 to help you visually identify the various anatomical structures mentioned in the text above.

Exercise
3

OOGENESIS

The paired **ovaries** are the female gonads; they are responsible for gamete formation and the production of the sex hormones *estrogen* and *progesterone*. As a fetus, the female ovaries contain many oogonia (2n) that all divide by mitosis to produce diploid daughter cells called **primary oocytes** that just begin meiosis I but remain dormant in late prophase I until puberty. The primary oocytes are surrounded by a single layer of **follicular cells** and are collectively known as **primordial follicles** (Fig. 17.7A).

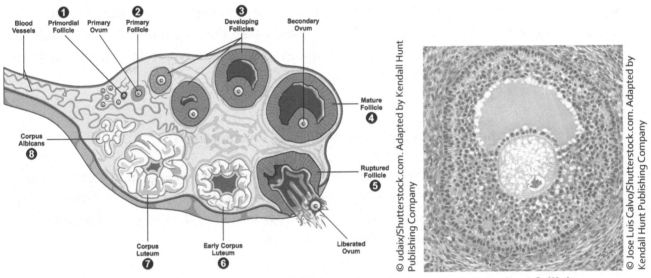

Figure 17.7   A) Development of the follicle and ovulation; B) a secondary follicle.

Each month, some of these follicles are stimulated to begin growth and become surrounded by more follicular cells to become **primary follicles** (Fig. 17.7A); however, typically only one primary follicle is "selected" to complete meiosis 1. This first meiotic division is unequal, with almost all the nutrient- and organelle-rich cytoplasm passing to the much larger **secondary oocyte** while the smaller **first polar body** receives little besides the chromosomes (Fig. 17.8). This polar body may go on to complete meiosis II, but without the cytoplasmic resources it often degenerates. The much larger **secondary follicle** (Fig. 17.7B) continues to enlarge by increasing the number of follicular cells, the creation of a fluid-filled cavity, and the formation of an encapsulating membrane called the **zona pellucida**.

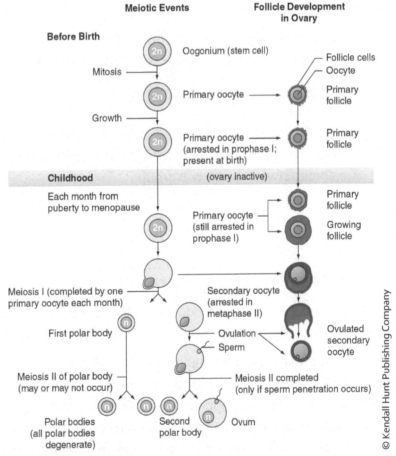

Figure 17.8   Meiotic events of oogenesis and follicle developmental stages.

The secondary oocyte begins meiosis II but will remain suspended in metaphase II until sperm penetration occurs. **Ovulation** is the rupturing of the follicle and the release of the secondary oocyte (still surrounded by a capsule of follicular cells) from the surface of the ovary (Fig. 17.7A). Although the oocyte has been ejected from the ovary, the remainder of the ruptured follicle continues to play an important role as an endocrine gland called the *corpus luteum* that, should fertilization and pregnancy occur, will provide hormones to guide embryonic development until the placenta takes over in about three months.

Study the Ovary: Ovary Model and Tissue Examination

Exercise 4

Find the ovary model on display in the laboratory and use Fig. 17.7A to help you identify the various structures associated with ovulation as described above (in bold lettering). Then, locate the microscope showing a cross-section of the ovary and attempt to find primary and secondary follicles (see Fig. 17.7B).

REVIEW QUESTIONS

1. During oogenesis in females, when does the oogonium divide by mitosis? When does the spermatogonium divide by mitosis in males?

2. What is the first haploid cell to be created during oogenesis?

3. Mammals like dogs, cats, and pigs all have multiple offspring at the same time while primates (apes and humans) typically have only one. Regarding ovulation, what must differ between these two groups?

THE FEMALE DUCT SYSTEM

Following ovulation, the reproductive cell and, if fertilized, the developing fetus is transported and serviced by the female's accessory ducts: the fallopian tubes, the uterus, and the vagina.

The **fallopian tubes,** also known as the *uterine tubes* or *oviducts*, extend from the anterior portion of the uterus but do not form a permanent connection to the ovaries. Each fallopian tube contacts an ovary with long appendages called **fimbriae** (Fig. 17.6), which are signaled by the release of certain hormones to sweep over the surface of the ovary near the site of ovulation. The secondary oocyte is guided into the fallopian tube by the fimbriae and then carried toward the uterus via ciliary action.

Following ovulation, the secondary oocyte is only viable for about 12 hours, making the oviducts the typical site of potential fertilization. Upon contact with the zona pellucida surrounding the secondary oocyte, the sperm cells release enzymes from their acrosomes to slowly digest this layer (the *acrosomal reaction*, Fig. 17.9). When a sperm cell reaches the plasma membrane, *sperm receptor proteins* initiate a series of chemical changes that prevent all other sperm cells from entering. The successful sperm then ejects its nucleus into the cytoplasm of the secondary oocyte.

When the successful sperm binds to the receptor protein, the secondary oocyte is stimulated to complete meiosis II, which forms a second polar body and the much larger **egg**. The sperm and egg nuclei then fuse together to create the diploid **zygote**, the first cell of the offspring.

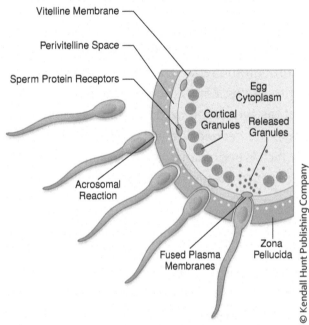

Figure 17.9   Fertilization. A sperm cell must digest its way through the zona pellucida to reach the cytoplasm of the immature egg.

© Kendall Hunt Publishing Company

REVIEW QUESTIONS

1. Why can't *polyspermy*, the entrance of multiple sperm into the secondary oocyte, occur?

2. The successful sperm that fertilizes the egg is often not the one that arrives first. Why might a sperm cell that arrives later be more successful?

Following fertilization in the oviduct, the diploid zygote undergoes a round of mitotic division to become a 2-celled **embryo**. Mitosis continues to create more and more cells as the embryo moves through the female reproductive system to eventually implant in the uterus and further develop into a *fetus*. Early embryonic development in humans consists of five stages: first there is *cleavage* of the zygote followed by four developmental forms called the *morula*, the *blastocyst*, the *gastrula*, and the *neurula*. We will consider only the events leading up to the formation of the *neural tube*, which is approximately 22 days after fertilization; embryonic development continues until it transitions to a fetus 8 weeks post-fertilization.

CLEAVAGE, MORULA, AND BLASTOCYST STAGES

Cleavage is the repeated mitotic division of the zygote into 2-cell, 4-cell, 8-cell, and 16-cell stages as it is transported toward the uterus (Fig. 17.10). Each round of cell division produces smaller and smaller cell sizes, thus increasing each cell's surface-area-to-volume ratio without increasing the overall size of the embryo itself.

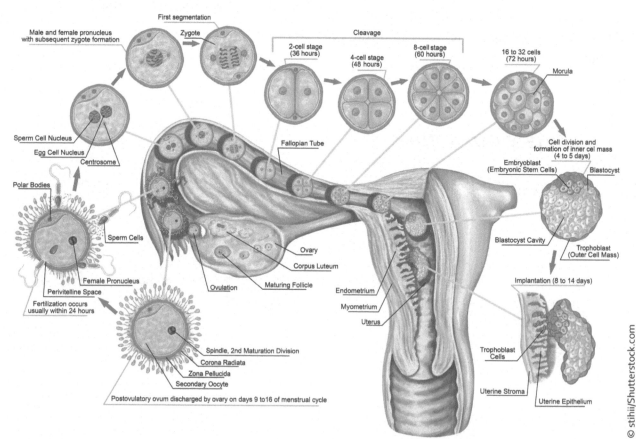

© stihii/Shutterstock.com

Figure 17.10   Early embryonic development: cleavage, morula, and blastocyst stages.

Fig. 17.10 shows the events that follow cleavage until implantation of the embryo in the uterus. At the 16-cell stage, approximately 72 hours post-fertilization, the small cluster of cells is known as the **morula**. As it continues to divide, several changes occur as the morula enters the uterus and becomes a **blastula**: the zona pellucida begins to break down, the cells produce fluid toward the center of the embryo as they flatten and form a single layer, and approximately 20–30 rounded cells called the inner cell mass clump together at one side. The **inner cell mass** is a collection of *stem cells* that give rise to the embryo proper.

The blastocyst stage is significant because for pregnancy to occur **implantation** of the blastocyst into the **endometrium**, the uterine lining, must take place. The endometrium thickens prior to ovulation in preparation for implantation, which begins about 7 days post-fertilization. The details of implantation are outside the scope of this course, but they involve the burrowing of the blastocyst into the endometrium and the fusion of the outermost layer of embryonic cells, called the *chorion*, with those of the uterine lining to form the *placenta*, which provides the embryo with nourishment from the mother's blood.

GASTRULATION

By day 14 the stem cells are arranged in a two-layered *embryonic disc* and the upper layer forms a narrow groove called the *primitive streak*. The process of *gastrulation* begins when cells pass through the primitive streak, which causes them to differentiate into three *primary germ layers*: the **ectoderm**, the **mesoderm**, and the **endoderm**. The **gastrula** is complete once these layers have been established and a long slender **notochord** has formed within the mesoderm (Figure 17.11). The significance of gastrulation lies in the differentiation of these early tissue layers, which give rise to each part of the body (see Table 17.1).

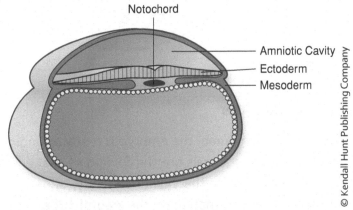

Notochord
Amniotic Cavity
Ectoderm
Mesoderm

© Kendall Hunt Publishing Company

Figure 17.11   The gastrula. Gastrulation gives rise to the ectoderm, mesoderm, and endoderm, which become the bodily tissues and organs. Other layers such as the amnion and the yolk sac are called the *extraembryonic* layers.

Table 17.1   Differentiated tissues and organs that arise from the primary germ layers.

Primary Germ Layer	Specialized Body Tissues and Organs
Ectoderm	Epidermis, Hair, Nails, Skin glands, Brain, Spinal cord
Mesoderm	Heart, Blood vessels, Wall of digestive and respiratory tracts, Muscle, Bone
Endoderm	Epithelial lining of digestive and respiratory tracts

View Starfish Development

Exercise 5

Locate the microscope showing various stages of starfish development and view under high power. Look for cells in the 2-cell, 4-cell, 8-cell, and morula stages using Fig. 17.12 as a guide. Find hollow balls of cells known as the blastula (like the blastocyst of mammals). Also find the most developed structures—these are the gastrula of the starfish.

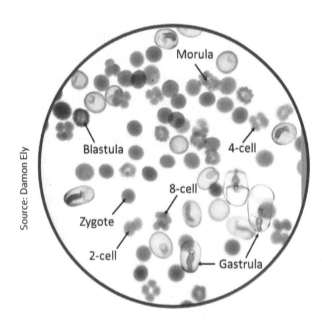

Figure 17.12 Embryonic development in the starfish. Cleavage of the zygote produces the multicellular morula, blastula, and gastrula stages of embryonic development in the starfish.

NEURULATION

Following gastrulation, the embryo is ready to begin organ formation, or *organogenesis*. The first events in organogenesis are the folding of the germ layers to form the cylindrical body, and the subsequent formation of the **neural tube** (i.e., the future brain and spinal cord) in a process called *neurulation*, which begins around days 20–22.

Neurulation is *induced*, or stimulated, by sig-

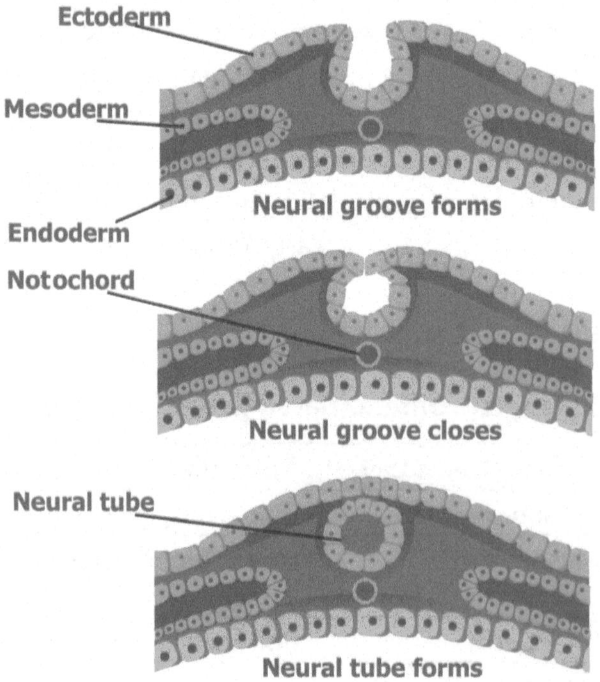

Ectoderm

Mesoderm

Endoderm

Notochord

Neural groove forms

Neural groove closes

Neural tube

Neural tube forms

Figure 17.13 Formation of the neural tube. During neurulation, the notochord induces a portion of the ectoderm to fold inward to form a long tube that will become the brain and spinal cord.

nals from the newly-formed mesodermal notochord (Fig. 17.11) which runs along the dorsal longitudinal axis of the embryo. The ectoderm overlying the notochord begins to thicken and fold inward until the tubular groove pinches off from the outer ectoderm (Fig. 17.13).

By the end of week 4, the **neurula** has developed blocks of mesodermal tissue (called *somites*) around the neural tube that will give rise to the vertebrae and ribs, and the endoderm folds into a tube to form the *primitive gut*. Fig. 17.13 shows these features in the frog neurula stage.

The embryo then continues to develop muscles, bones, limb buds, and organ systems in rudimentary forms. After 8 weeks, the 2.5 cm embryo becomes the fetus. Fetal development (weeks 9–40) hardens the bones, shapes the body, and ensures the efficiency of all organ systems.

View the Frog Neurula

Exercise 6

Locate the microscope on display showing the frog neurula as it develops. Scan the slide to see the various stages of inward folding of the ectoderm to eventually form the neural tube. Use Fig. 17.14 to locate the fully-formed neurula and identify the ectoderm, meso-derm, endoderm, notochord, neural tube, primitive gut, yolk, *and* somites.

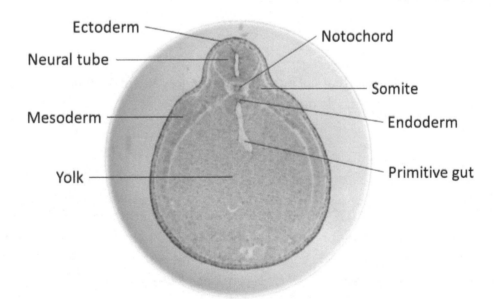

Figure 17.14 Frog neurula. Despite many differences in the patterns of embryonic development, the frog neurula closely resembles that of a human. One difference is the presence of yolk in the frog embryo. Because humans receive nutrition from the mother's blood via the placenta, the yolk sac in human embryos does not develop yolk.

1. During the cleavage and morula stages, the embryonic cells must divide quickly and position themselves correctly. Why does it help these cells to become smaller with each round of division during this time?

2 In the blastocyst stage, only the inner cell mass contains cells that will give rise to the body of the fetus. What role is played by the outermost cells called the chorion?

3. Which germ layer gives rise to most of your body's tissues and organs?

4. Why do animals that lay eggs (birds, reptiles, and amphibians) develop a large yolk while most mammals do not?

5. *CONSIDER FURTHER*: By the end of four to six months, most of a fetus's organ systems are operational except one. Which system do you think develops last? How is the fetus able to grow and function correctly without this system for so long? *Hint: Think of how a premature baby must be cared for before it can leave a hospital.*

CHAPTER 18
PATTERNS OF INHERITANCE: MENDELIAN GENETICS AND BEYOND

 ## Laboratory Objectives

By the end of this laboratory, the student should be able to:

- explain how the inheritance of traits is related to meiosis;
- define the following terms: *gene, allele, P generation, F1 and F2 generations, genotype, phenotype, homozygous, heterozygous, dominant and recessive*;
- use a Punnett square to cross parents of known genotypes and determine the genotypic and phenotypic probabilities for offspring;
- use a Chi-Square test for goodness of fit between expected and observed outcomes of a monohybrid cross;
- use a dihybrid cross to illustrate the concept of independent assortment;
- understand non-Mendelian patterns of inheritance: *incomplete dominance, codominance, and polygenic inheritance*;
- determine how X-linked traits are inherited and expressed in a sex-linked manner.

Our physical traits are mostly controlled by **genes**—sequences of DNA nucleotides found in our chromosomes (Chapter 14). Before the discovery of chromosomes, however, an Austrian monk named **Gregor Mendel** (1822–1884) carried out hundreds of experiments investigating patterns of inheritance of traits in the pea plant *Pisum sativum*. Through his elegant experimental design and meticulous recordkeeping, Mendel unknowingly gained insight into the major events of meiosis (Chapter 16) and established two laws that remain the cornerstones of genetics: the *law of segregation* and the *law of independent assortment*.

Since Mendel's time, scientists have found more complicated patterns of inheritance. Indeed, the field of genetics continues to make new discoveries that help us understand the roles our genes play in the variation we observe among individuals. This laboratory will introduce you to **Mendelian genetics** (the inheritance and control of a single trait by a single gene) and provide you with an understanding of some other patterns of inheritance discovered after Mendel's time.

Mendel's success was due in large part to his choice of the pea plant as his test subject; peas have a relatively short generation time and a number of easily-observed traits that are each controlled by a single gene. In addition, like most plants, a single pea flower produces both sperm and egg gametes and is capable of self-fertilization; which allowed Mendel to track the frequency of occurrence of certain traits through several generations without any complications from outside the gene pool established by the original parents.

Mendel's breakthrough discovery came while he was observing the **trait** of flower color in the pea plant, of which there were two **alleles** (forms of a gene): purple and white. Prior to conducting his experiment, Mendel first established two lines of pea plants that were *true-breeding* for flower color, meaning that self-fertilization consistently produced offspring with flowers of only one color. To begin his experiment, Mendel performed a **cross** (sexual reproduction between two individuals) between a true-breeding purple flower plant and a true-breeding white flower plant; these individuals are known as the **P (parental) generation** (Fig. 18.1). Surprisingly, 100% of the **F1 (first filial)** generation flowers were purple (Fig. 18.1), the white trait was not expressed in any of the F1 individuals!

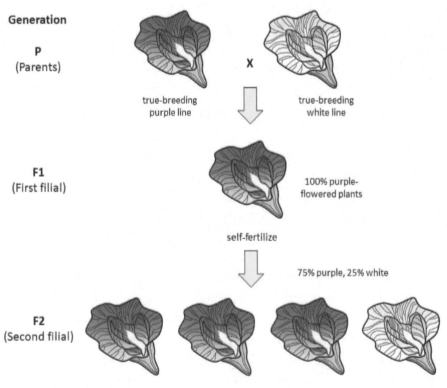

Generation

P
(Parents)

X

true-breeding
purple line

true-breeding
white line

F1
(First filial)

100% purple-
flowered plants

self-fertilize

75% purple, 25% white

F2
(Second filial)

Figure 18.1   Mendel's hallmark experiment. A cross between two parents (P generation) that possess different alleles for a trait, each parent having two copies of that allele, will produce all monohybrid F1 offspring that express the dominant trait. Self-fertilization of the F1 individuals leads to a frequently-observed 3:1 (dominant:recessive) ratio in the F2 generation.

Source: Damon Ely

Mendel then allowed the F1 individuals to self-fertilize, planted their seeds, and let the **F2 (second filial)** generation plants grow and produce flowers. By carefully noting the outcome of flower color in these repeated trials, a pattern emerged: an average 3:1 ratio of offspring with purple and white flowers, respectively (Fig. 18.1).

These results suggested to Mendel that the allele for the white flower trait had not been lost in the F1 generation; instead, the F1 individuals were **monohybrids**, meaning that they possessed both alleles for this single gene, but the allele for white flowers was not being expressed. Thus, Mendel posited that the different forms of a trait (i.e., the different alleles of a gene) must follow a hierarchy of dominance: one trait is **dominant** over the other, which is called **recessive**.

CONSIDER FURTHER

?

1. Before his experiment, Mendel had observed that sometimes plants with purple flowers had offspring with white flowers. Why was it important to Mendel that the P generation plants in his experiment were true-breeding?

2. Consider the following data showing the distribution of flower color in the F2 offspring of five self-fertilized F1 individuals:

F1 Trials	F2: # of purple-flowered plants	F2: # of white-flowered plants	Ratio of purple:white
Trial 1	72	27	2.7:1
Trial 2	137	41	3.3:1
Trial 3	69	22	3.1:1
Trial 4	90	35	2.6:1
Trial 5	96	31	3.1:1

Judging from the data above, why is it important to create many replicate trials when designing any experiment? What are the possible consequences of no replication?

3. Mendel called the F1 individuals in his experiment 'carriers'. What do you think he meant by the term carrier?

Mendel's experiment led to his first law of inheritance, the **law of segregation**. In summary, the law of segregation states:

1. Each individual has two factors for every trait.
2. These factors separate during the production of gametes; thus, gametes only possess one factor for each trait.
3. Fertilization gives each new individual two factors for every trait.

We can now see that Mendel had gained insight into the process of meiosis decades before it had been formally discovered. The law of segregation describes how homologous chromosomes in diploid cells separate during the creation of haploid gametes, egg, and sperm. This means that each gamete produced carries only one allele for each trait. In the offspring, the combination of alleles for a trait that results from fertilization is referred to as the **genotype**. An individual's **phenotype** is the physical characteristic expressed (e.g., purple or white flowers) in the individual as a result of their genotype.

Three specific terms are used to describe the genotype for a trait. An individual is **homozygous dominant** for a trait if they possess two dominant alleles. **Homozygous recessive** refers to two recessive alleles for a trait. An individual is **heterozygous** for a trait if they possess one dominant and one recessive allele. Upper-case and lower-case letters are used to represent dominant and recessive alleles, respectively. The relationships between genotype and phenotype are presented in Table 18.1 using the dominant purple-flower (P) and recessive white-flower (p) traits in the pea plant.

Genotype	Genotype	Phenotype
PP	Homozygous dominant	Purple-flowered plant
Pp	Heterozygous	Purple-flowered plant
pp	Homozygous recessive	White-flowered plant

Table 18.1   Genotype and Phenotype. The genotype describes the specific combination of alleles for a trait. The phenotype describes the physical characteristic expressed in the individual. In this example, the dominant P allele codes for purple flowers and the recessive p allele codes for white flowers.

TEST YOUR UNDERSTANDING

?

Look back at Mendel's experiment (Fig. 18.1) and identify the genotypes for the following plants by writing both the combination of letters and the terms *homozygous dominant*, *heterozygous*, or *homozygous recessive*:

P generation: true-breeding purple-flowered plant: ____ _____

P generation: true-breeding white-flowered plant: ____ _____

F1 generation: purple-flowered plant: ____ _____

USING THE PUNNETT SQUARE

A **Punnett square** is a simple tool used to predict the genotypic and phenotypic outcomes of a cross between parents of known genotypes.

A Punnett square consists of four quadrants; each allele of one parent is written at the top of each column, and each allele of the other parent is written on the side to represent each row. Each of the four quadrants are then filled in with the appropriate combination of alleles using the column and row headings. Fig. 18.2 shows how to construct a Punnett square for a cross between two pea plants that are both heterozygous for the flower color gene.

Although it is simple to construct a Punnett square, it is important to understand what it

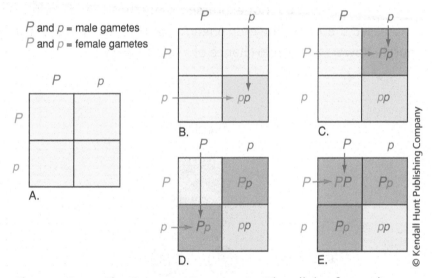

Figure 18.2 The Punnett Square. A—The alleles for each parent are written as column and row headings. B, C, D, and E—Each quadrant is filled in with the combination of alleles given the column and row, representing a possible genotype for the offspring.

represents biologically. Remember that the two alleles of a parent reside on two homologous chromosomes, which are separated from each other during meiosis and placed into individual gametes. Each quadrant of the Punnett square represents the possible outcome of a fertilization event between these two parents.

The probability of each outcome can be calculated using the Punnett square. **Probability** is calculated by first dividing the number of observed outcomes for either a specific genotype or phenotype by the total number of outcomes possible, which is always 4, and then multiplying by 100 to express it as a percentage.

For example, Fig. 18.3 shows two Punnett squares representing Mendel's famous experiment with the purple- and white-flowered pea plants. The Punnett square on the left represents the original P generation cross between the two true-breeding lines: the homozygous dominant purple-flowered plants and the homozygous recessive white-flowered plants. The resulting F1 offspring are 100% heterozygous purple-flowered plants (the monohybrids discussed earlier).

The Punnett square on the right in Fig. 18.3 shows a monohybrid cross (a cross between two heterozygotes) that represents the self-fertilization of the F1 individuals. For the F2 generation, we see 1 out of 4 (25%) are homozygous dominant, 2 out of 4 (50%) are heterozygous, and 25% are homozygous recessive. We can also express these results using a **genotypic ratio** of 1:2:1 (PP:Pp:pp).

We can now explain why Mendel observed the **phenotypic ratio** of 3:1 (purple:white flowers) in the F2 generation. Each of the heterozygous F1 plants was a **carrier** of the recessive trait, meaning that it was present but not expressed. Only those F2 offspring that received both recessive alleles expressed the white-flowered phenotype. Thus, each seed created has a 75% chance of developing purple flowers and a 25% chance of white flowers.

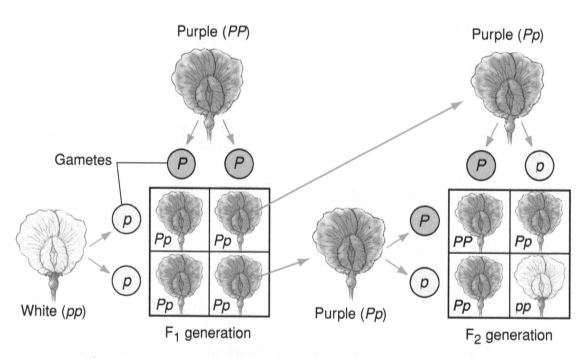

Figure 18.3   Mendel's monohybrid cross using Punnett squares.

APPLY YOUR UNDERSTANDING

?

1. Phenylketonuria (PKU) is a metabolic disease that affects the body's ability to process phenylalanine, an amino acid, causing a buildup of phenylalanine in the blood. While harmful brain damage is possible, life expectancy is generally not shortened.

PKU results from the inheritance of two recessive alleles for the gene that encodes phenylalanine hydroxylase, the enzyme that processes phenylalanine, on chromosome 12. Let K represent the dominant allele, and k represent the recessive allele.

Use the Punnett square to perform a cross between a heterozygous individual and an individual with PKU.

What is the probability that these two parents will have a child with PKU? _____

What is the probability of having a homozygous dominant child? _____

2. In the pea plant, seed color is either yellow (Y) or green (y). Use the Punnett square to cross two plants that are both carriers of the recessive trait.

If 160 offspring are produced:

How many plants are predicted to have green seeds? _____

How many offspring will be carriers? _____

3. Albinism is inherited in an autosomal (not sex-linked) recessive manner, causing the lack of pigmentation in the eyes and skin. Let A represent the dominant non-albino allele and let a represent the recessive allele.

Can a homozygous non-albino individual create albino offspring? Explain why or why not.

Test the Law of Segregation

Exercise 1

Create a gene pool using red and yellow beads and work in groups of four students to form "offspring" of differing genotypes as described in the procedure. You will then use chi-square analysis to test whether your data support Mendel's law of segregation.

OBJECTIVE:

To test whether the law of segregation can predict patterns of inheritance.

MATERIALS:

300mL beaker   40 red beads   40 yellow beads   3 plastic cups   3 index cards   calculator

PROCEDURE:

PART 1

1. Create a gene pool by placing the 40 red beads (representing dominant R alleles) and the 40 yellow beads (representing recessive r alleles) in the beaker. By having an equal number of R and r alleles in the gene pool, you will simulate a monohybrid cross—a cross between two heterozygous individuals.

   Use the Punnett square to perform a cross between two heterozygous individuals (Rr) for these alleles represented with the beads.

   What should be the genotype ratio (in simplest terms) of the offspring?

   _____:_____:_____

2. Label each of the three index cards with the different possible genotypes: RR, Rr, and rr (make the labels large and clear so that each student can see). Place a cup by each index card in the center of the table so each member of the group clearly knows which genotype is represented by each cup.

3. Mix the beads thoroughly before starting the activity. Have one person draw out two beads at random (without looking) and quickly pass the beaker to the person on their left.

4. Continue in this way, passing the beaker from person to person around the table with each person randomly selecting two beads at a time. After you pass the beaker, snap your two beads together and place this new 'individual' into the appropriate genotype/plastic cup. Continue until all the beads have been removed from the beaker.

PART 2

1. Count how many of each genotype (RR, Rr, rr) your group created and record this value in the column labeled **# Observed** in Table 18.2.

2. Because you randomly selected pairs of alleles, your observed genotype distribution is probably different from the expected 10:20:10 (RR:Rr:rr) as predicted by Mendel's law of segregation. But *how* different? In science, variation is always expected, and statistics are used to determine when the differences are so large that they become *significant* differences due to some real effect.

   In our activity, we need to test whether a) the difference between what we observe and what we expect due to the law of segregation is only a slight variation and therefore supports Mendel's law, or b) the difference we observe is significant and therefore does not support Mendel's law.

   To make this decision, we will use a statistical test called **chi-square (X^2) analysis** to compare our observed and expected values. This analysis results in a *test statistic* that is used to determine significance. Work through the calculations in Table 18.2 to determine the test statistic.

Table 18.2   Calculation of X^2.

Genotypes	# Expected (E)	# Observed (O)	O − E	(O − E)²	(O − E)² ÷ E
RR	10				
Rr	20				
rr	10				
					SUM =

3. The X^2 test statistic is the sum of the last column. Enter it here: _____

4. You must also calculate the degrees of freedom (df). The df is equal to n − 1, where n is the number of categories. In our activity, there were only three possible outcomes: RR, Rr, and rr. Since the number of genotypes equals 3, our df = 3 − 1 = 2.

5. Use Table 18.3 to determine whether your test statistic is significant at a *p* value of 0.05: look at the df = 2 row and compare your test statistic to the value in the 0.05 column. *If your test statistic is lower than this value, your results are not significantly different than expected and your data supports Mendel's law of segregation. If your test statistic is equal to or greater than this value, your results are significantly different than expected and your data does not support Mendel's law of segregation.*

6. State whether your X^2 test statistic was significant or insignificant and your conclusion about Mendel's law of segregation: _____

_____

Table 18.3 Critical Values of X² Test Statistics

df	p values				
	0.50	**0.20**	**0.10**	**0.05**	**0.01**
1	0.455	1.642	2.706	3.841	6.635
2	1.386	3.219	4.605	5.991	9.210
3	2.366	4.642	6.251	7.815	11.341
	not significantly different (supported)			significantly different (rejected)	

THE LAW OF INDEPENDENT ASSORTMENT

You were first introduced to the concept of independent assortment in Chapter 16—Meiosis. There you learned that **independent assortment** is the random separation of maternal and paternal homologues during meiosis I. Mendel observed this phenomenon in his pea plants, which led him to create his second law, *the law of independent assortment*. In summary, the law states that if two genes do not occur on the same chromosome, then all combinations of the alleles present for these two traits are possible in the gametes.

Mendel observed more than one trait at a time in his pea plants. For example, when he performed a P generation cross between a true-breeding plant that was tall with green pods and a true-breeding plant that was short with yellow pods, he found F2 individuals of all combinations (tall plants with yellow pods, short plants with green pods, etc.). In the same way that the F1 individuals in Fig. 18.1 were monohybrids, the F1 generation plants in this example were **dihybrids**—they were heterozygous for both the height (tall, T; short, t) and pod color (green, G; yellow, g) traits. Since we are now considering two traits simultaneously, we write the genotype of these dihybrids as TtGg. The gametes from these dihybrids would show all combinations of these alleles: TG, Tg, tG, and tg.

Fig. 18.4 shows how a *double-factor cross* (two traits considered simultaneously) is set up using a larger Punnett square. This particular cross is an example of a **dihybrid cross** in guinea pigs. A pattern emerges when this experiment is repeated: a characteristic 9:3:3:1 ratio of phenotypes is observed due to the dominance hierarchy. As you can tell from the number of different

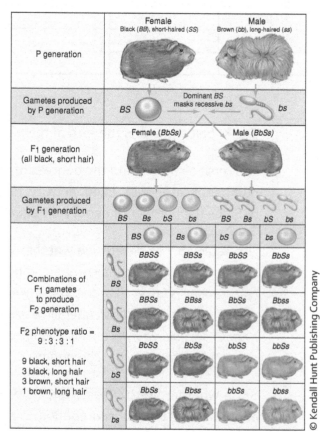

© Kendall Hunt Publishing Company

Figure 18.4   A dihybrid cross in guinea pigs.

guinea pig phenotypes in Fig. 18.4, independent assortment creates a large amount of variation among the individuals in a population.

TEST YOUR UNDERSTANDING

In the pea plant, smooth seeds (S) is dominant to wrinkled seeds (s), and yellow seeds (Y) is dominant to green seeds (y). These two genes are independent of each other, meaning they occur on different chromosomes.

1. What are the four possible allele combinations that a dihybrid pea plant (SsYy) can create?

_____ _____ _____ _____

2. Fill out the Punnett square below to show the expected distribution of offspring produced when this dihybrid pea plant self-fertilizes.

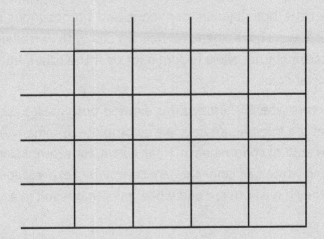

3. Use the Punnet square above to answer the following: If 48 offspring are produced, how many of each of the following phenotypes would you expect to see?

smooth, yellow _____ smooth, green _____ wrinkled, yellow _____ wrinkled, green _____

4. What are the possible alleles that could be created by a pea plant with a SSYy genotype?

 If this plant was crossed with another individual, could it produce offspring with wrinkled seeds?

5. What if the genes for seed shape and seed color were on the same chromosome? Would their alleles still follow the law of independent assortment? How might their pattern of inheritance differ?

Non-Mendelian genetics refers to more complicated patterns of inheritance that aren't necessarily a one-gene/one-trait relationship or governed by fully dominant or recessive alleles. Phenomena such as *polygenic inheritance*, *incomplete dominance*, and *codominance* represent inheritance patterns that were discovered after Mendel's seminal work.

Thus far we have considered traits that are of either one form or another (e.g., flowers that are either purple or white). But what about traits that we know are genetically determined and show a variety of permutations, like human height or the shape of the nose? These traits and many others are the result of **polygenic inheritance**, where more than one gene contributes to a single trait. In these cases, the protein products of multiple genes interact in a variety of combinations to produce a continuous distribution of phenotypes for the single trait. Predicting the probabilities of different offspring under polygenic inheritance looks much the same as a double-factor cross (Fig. 18.4); however, each outcome represents the phenotype of just a single trait.

Incomplete dominance is a pattern of inheritance where the phenotype of heterozygotes is *intermediate* between the homozygous dominant and homozygous recessive phenotypes. For example, four o'clock flowers have a gene for flower color with two alleles: C^R codes for red, and C^W codes for white. Because neither allele is dominant over the other, heterozygotes (C^RC^W) have an intermediate pink flower color.

Codominance occurs when heterozygotes express both alleles *completely* (as opposed to an intermediate blend of the two phenotypes like incomplete dominance). Roan coat color occurs in many mammals as a result of codominance. Roan cattle, for example, are heterozygotes that have alleles for both red and white hair color that are completely expressed in individual hairs throughout the animal (i.e., they have both red and white hairs that result in a mottled appearance).

TEST YOUR UNDERSTANDING

Polygenic Inheritance

Human eye color is controlled by at least 8 different genes that interact to affect how much melanin (the protein responsible for eye, hair, and skin color) is produced by cells in the iris, the muscular aperture that controls the amount of light entering the eye. Let us simplify the inheritance of eye color to being governed by two independent genes: OCA2 (S and s alleles) and TYRP1 (B and b alleles).

1. Parent 1 has the genotype Ssbb. List the possible alleles they can create. _____

2. Parent 2 has the genotype ssBb. List the possible alleles they can create. _____

3. In the space below, set up and complete the appropriate Punnett square needed to cross these two parents.

4. Use the following phenotype guidelines to answer the questions below.

   Brown eyes: SSBB, SSBb, SsBB, or SsBb
   Hazel eyes: ssBb or ssBB
   Blue eyes: SSbb, Ssbb, or ssbb

   Identify the eye color of each parent: Parent 1: _____   Parent 2: _____

   When these two parents have a child, what is the probability that this child will have:

   brown eyes: _____   hazel eyes: _____   blue eyes: _____

5. Should eye color be used as the basis for a paternity test? Why or why not?

Incomplete Dominance and Codominance

The difference between incomplete dominance and codominance often depends on what level of organization (molecular, cellular, or organismal) is considered. A good example of this is *sickle-cell anemia*, a disease caused by a mutation in the gene for hemoglobin, the protein that carries oxygen inside red blood cells (RBCs). The mutation causes RBCs to collapse into a sickle shape, causing poor circulation and a lowered ability to provide oxygen to the body's cells.

The hemoglobin gene, Hb, has two alleles: Hb^A and Hb^S. The relationship between genotype and phenotype is as follows:

Hb^A/Hb^A: Normal, no abnormal hemoglobin, red blood cells do not sickle

Hb^S/Hb^S: Severe anemia, all hemoglobin abnormal, red blood cells have sickle shape

Hb^A/Hb^S: Infrequent anemia, both normal and abnormal hemoglobin molecules are produced, red blood cells sickle under oxygen stress

6. Consider the molecular level: Individuals that are heterozygous for the trait produce both kinds of hemoglobin molecules. A blood analysis will show equal concentrations of both normal and abnormal hemoglobin molecules. Is this <u>incomplete dominance</u> or <u>codominance</u>?

Now consider the cellular level: Hb^A/Hb^A individuals have normal RBCs that never sickle, and Hb^S/Hb^S individuals have RBCs that all have the sickle shape. Individuals that are heterozygous for the trait have red blood cells that are of normal shape until oxygen concentrations in the blood are lower, at which point the RBCs collapse into a sickle shape. At the cellular level, is this <u>incomplete dominance</u> or <u>codominance</u>?

18.3 SEX-LINKED TRAITS

In humans, the 23rd pair of chromosomes are the **sex chromosomes**, so-named because these chromosomes determine an individual's sex (the other 22 pairs are called *autosomes*). There are two different sex chromosomes, X and Y, and they are only partially homologous. In females, both sex chromosomes are the X chromosome; males have one X and one Y chromosome. The Y chromosome is much smaller than the X (Fig. 18.5) and does not hold most of the genes found on the X. Despite their differences, the X and Y chromosomes pair up during prophase 1 and separate during anaphase 1, meaning that individual sperm cells will either carry an X or a Y, thus determining the sex of the offspring.

Since males have only one X chromosome, they possess only one allele for each gene found on the X and will express that allele whether it is dominant or recessive. While females may still be homozygous or heterozygous for an X-linked trait, these terms do not apply to males for genes occurring on the X.

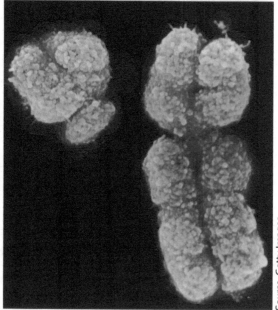

Figure 18.5 The sex chromosomes. The much larger X chromosome carries many genes not found on the Y.

Source: Getty Images

COLOR BLINDNESS: A SEX-LINKED TRAIT

A common example of a sex-linked trait is color blindness, or more accurately, color deficiency. A person with color blindness can still see color but may have difficulty distinguishing red and green colors (most common) or blue and yellow colors (total color blindness is very rare). Roughly 8% of men (1 in 12) and 0.5% of women (1 in 200) have red-green color blindness.

The greater incidence of color blindness in males stems from the fact that the photopigments used to respond to the red, green, and blue wavelengths of light by the cone cells in the retina of our eyes are encoded by genes on the X chromosome. Heterozygous females may carry the recessive allele (X^b) for color blindness, but it is masked by the dominant allele (X^B). However, if a male receives the X^b allele on his only X chromosome, then he will express a color deficiency.

A Punnett square for the inheritance of a sex-linked trait is shown in Fig. 18.6 using color blindness as an example. In this example, the male parent is color-blind, and the female is a carrier of the color blindness trait. Since the X and Y chromosomes separate during meiosis, some sperm cells will carry the recessive allele while those with the Y chromosome will not carry either allele for the trait. The female parent will create an egg that either has the dominant B allele for color vision or the recessive b allele for color blindness. The probability that these two parents will have a color-blind child is 50%, regardless of whether they have a boy or a girl.

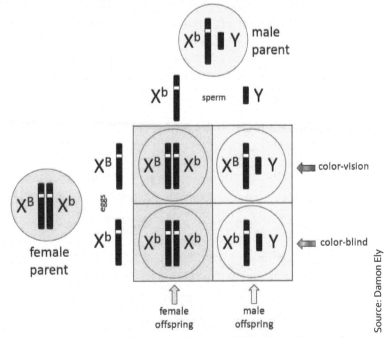

Figure 18.6   Inheritance of a sex-linked trait. A color-blind male and a female carrier have a 50% chance of having a color-blind child.

Source: Damon Ely

APPLY YOUR UNDERSTANDING

1. What if the male parent in Fig. 18.6 had color vision? What is the probability that these two parents would have a color-blind child? Would one sex be more affected than another?

2. Is it possible for a color-blind female to have a son with color vision? Why or why not?

3. Muscular dystrophy (MD) is a sex-linked disorder in the development of muscle cells. Roughly 1 in 3,500 boys suffers from the disorder, which causes them to synthesize a defective form of dystrophin, a protein that provides the strong support needed by muscle cells to withstand the forceful contraction of muscle fibers.

Without functional dystrophin, muscle contractions tear muscle cells, causing the cells to die. Instead of new muscle, the cells are replaced by fat and connective tissue. The ability to walk is often lost by age 8, and difficulties with respiratory and heart functions usually lead to death in the early 20s.

The gene for dystrophin has two alleles: the dominant D allele that correctly builds dystrophin, and the recessive d allele that creates defective dystrophin. Complete the Punnett square to show a cross between a female who carries the recessive allele and a male who does not have MD.

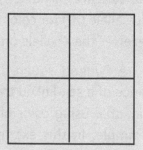

What are the chances that these two parents will have a daughter with MD?

What would you have to change about the parents for there to be any chance of producing a daughter with MD?

Considering your last answer, and the information provided above about MD, why is it highly unlikely that females will have this disorder?

4. Lethal alleles are expected to be purged from populations through natural selection, yet the lethal MD allele persists at a constant frequency. Even though female carriers may pass on this allele, thousands of years of natural selection should have reduced its incidence to nearly zero. So why does it persist? Answer the following questions to find out.

Mutations arise most often during the process of DNA replication. What do you think is the relationship between the length of a gene and the chances of a mutation occurring?

The dystrophin gene is 2.2 *million* nucleotides long while the average human gene is roughly 27 *thousand* nucleotides. What does this mean for the mutation rate of dystrophin?

Roughly one-third of boys with MD received a X^d chromosome from a mother who is X^DX^D. How is this possible?

LABORATORY GLOSSARY

A

absorption The process of moving materials out from one area and into another.

accessory organs An organ that aids in digestion but is not a part of the primary digestive tract.

accommodation (eye) Process by which the eye focuses on objects at varying distances by changing the shape of the lens.

acid A substance that releases H⁺ ions, lowering the pH of a solution.

acrosomes The organelle on the head of a sperm cell that aids in breaking down the egg coating to allow entrance into the ovum for fertilization.

action potential The change in the electrical gradient associated with the electrochemical impulse that travels through the extent of the nerve cell.

active transport The transport of molecules that requires the use of energy to move molecules against a concentration gradient.

adrenal gland The gland of the endocrine system that produces various hormones including adrenaline, cortisol, and the precursors to sex hormones; located above the kidneys.

allele One of the alternate versions of a gene that codes for the characteristics of an organism.

Allium A genus of plants that includes onions, garlic, scallions, and many other edible species.

alveolus (plural, alveoli) The sac-like structures of the lungs that serve as the location for gas exchange.

amino acids The monomers of proteins that link together to form polypeptides.

amylase The enzyme released in the digestive system by the salivary glands and pancreas that hydrolyzes starches.

anaphase Stage of mitosis when sister chromatids separate.

Animalia The kingdom in the domain Eukarya that represents multicellular heterotrophic organisms without a cell wall.

anion A negatively-charged ion.

anterior An anatomical position of the body located toward the front of an organism.

anticodon A group of three bases that serve as the reading units found on tRNA.

antiparallel The orientation of the single strands of DNA that are aligned opposite of each other.

anus The exiting site of the digestive system through which fecal waste is eliminated.

aorta The blood vessel that carries blood away from the left ventricle to the systemic system.

aortic semilunar valve The valve of the heart preventing backflow of blood from the aorta to the left ventricle.

appendix The small tube-shaped pouch below the cecum that may aid in storing healthy bacteria for the large intestine.

Archaea The domain of prokaryotes most closely related to eukaryotes.

arm (microscope) The part that is above the base used to carry a microscope.

arrector pili muscle A smooth muscle attached to hair follicles that when contracted produces goose bumps.

artery Blood vessels that carry blood away from the heart.

ascending colon The first major portion on the right side of the large intestine carrying undigested material to the transverse colon.

atom The smallest unit of matter.

atomic number The number of protons in an atom.

atrioventricular (AV) node The portion of the conduction system of the heart that receives impulses from the SA node to initiate ventricular contraction.

atrium (plural, atria) The chambers of the heart that receive blood from the venous system.

auditory canal The tube-shaped part of the external ear that carries sound waves to the tympanic membrane.

auditory ossicles The bones of the middle ear that receive and amplify vibrations toward the cochlea.

autonomic nervous system The part of the peripheral nervous system that controls involuntary responses.

axon A long fiber-like extension that propagates the nerve impulse towards axon terminals and ultimately another neuron, muscle cell, or gland.

B

bacillus Rod-shaped bacteria.

Bacteria The domain of prokaryotes composed of simple unicellular organisms.

base A substance that releases OH^- ions raising the pH of a solution.

base (microscope) The part of a microscope that serves as the foundation.

bicuspid valve The valve of the heart preventing backflow of blood from the left ventricle to the left atrium.

bile A solution of water, bile salts, cholesterol, and other substances.

binary fission Cell division of prokaryotic organisms.

biology The study of living organisms and their interactions.

blastocyst A stage of embryo development consisting of a mass of undifferentiated cells with a fluid filled cavity containing an inner cell mass.

blind spot Location in the eye where the optic nerve leaves the retina; devoid of photoreceptors.

blood The fluid tissue of the circulatory system that consists of blood cells and dissolved materials of the plasma.

bolus The masticated material in the oral cavity that is a mixture of food and saliva.

Bowman's capsule The cup-like portion of a nephron that surrounds the glomerulus where filtration of blood is initiated in the kidney.

brain The major processing organ in the central nervous system.

brain stem The part of the brain connecting to the spinal cord consisting of the medulla oblongata, pons, and the midbrain.

bronchioles The portion of the respiratory system that branches off from the bronchus carrying air to the alveoli.

bronchus (plural, bronchi) The portion of the respiratory system that branches off from the trachea carrying air to the lungs.

brow spot A spot located medial and anterior to the eyes on a frog that is regarded as the vestigial "third eye".

Brownian motion The random motion of particles suspended in a liquid or gas caused by kinetic energy.

buffer A substance that resists changes of pH when either acids or bases are added.

bulbourethral glands A gland of the male reproductive system that releases pre-ejaculatory fluid into the urethra.

C

capillary Small blood vessels where gases, nutrients, and other dissolved solutes exchange with the tissue fluids surrounding the body's cells.

carbohydrate An organic molecule consisting of carbon, hydrogen, and oxygen with common hydroxyl groups; serves as an energy-rich molecule and provides structural support in cells.

carbon dioxide A molecule produced during aerobic respiration that is exhaled from the respiratory system.

carboxypeptidase An enzyme produced in the pancreas that hydrolyzes peptide bonds in proteins.

cardiac muscle The muscle found in the heart, with intercalated discs, that contracts to pump blood through the circulatory system.

cartilage Connective tissue found in ligaments, tendons, joints, and other areas.

cation A positively-charged ion.

cecum The pouch of the large intestine located below the connection to the small intestine.

cell The smallest fundamental unit of life.

cell body The largest volume of the nerve cell that contains the nucleus and many of the other organelles of the eukaryotic cell.

cell cycle Sequence of cellular events from one cell division into the next division.

cell membrane A phospholipid bilayer containing proteins that acts as a semipermeable barrier between the cell and the outer environment.

cell plate The structure separating plant cells during cytokinesis.

cell wall A rigid structure outside the cell membrane of some organisms that provides structural support to a cell.

cellulose A filamentous polysaccharide providing support to plant cell walls.

central nervous system (CNS) The nervous system consisting of the brain and spinal cord.

central vacuole A large organelle within a plant cell that acts as a storage compartment.

centriole The microtubules found in centrosomes in animal cells.

centromere The region connecting sister chromatids.

cerebellum A large portion of the brain involved with motor coordination, attached to the dorsal side of the brain stem and inferior to the occipital lobe.

cerebral cortex The outer layer of the cerebrum involved with higher-level processing.

cervix The "neck" of the uterus; the opening of the uterus.

chemical digestion The hydrolytic breakdown of organic molecules that occurs throughout the digestive system.

chloroplast A double membrane-bound organelle that performs photosynthesis.

choroid The layer of vascular tissue between the retina and the sclera.

chromatin The structural organization of DNA, and associated histones, containing an organism's genes found in the nucleus.

chromosome The structure of DNA when tightly condensed around histone proteins.

chyme The acidic mixture of partially-digested food items and gastric juices found in the stomach.

chymotrypsin A hydrolytic enzyme that digests proteins in the small intestine; secreted by the pancreas.

cilium (plural, cilia) A short hair-like mobile extension of the plasma membrane.

cleavage The repeated mitotic division of the zygote into 2-cell, 4-cell, 8-cell, and 16-cell stages which produces smaller and smaller cell sizes.

cleavage furrow The interactions of actin and myosin filaments that form a contractile ring to separate the cells during cytokinesis in animal cells.

cloacal opening The single excretory orifice in a frog that releases digestive, urinary, and reproductive system contents.

coarse focus knobs (microscope) The rough adjustment that brings the objective lenses closer or farther away from the slides.

coccus Spherical-shaped bacteria.

cochlea The spiral-shaped structure of the inner ear that has stereocilia which detects vibrations and produces nerve impulses.

cochlear nerve Transmits chemical electrical impulses between the inner ear and the brain.

codominance A pattern of inheritance where two different alleles of a gene are equally expressed.

codon A group of three nucleotides which are the reading units for specific amino acids found on mRNA.

collecting duct Microscopic tubule of the kidney that receives filtrate from the distal tubules of several nephrons; transfers filtrate to the renal pelvis.

colon The portion of the large intestine consisting of the ascending, transverse, descending, and sigmoid regions.

colonial An organism that can transition between a collection of cells working together and a single independent cell.

complementary base-pairing The specific connections of nitrogenous bases found in nucleotides (C-G and A-T, or A-U) due to hydrogen bonding.

compound microscope The instrument used to magnify and view specimens that are slide-mounted.

concentration gradient A difference in the number of particles between two areas.

condenser (microscope) The part gathering and focusing light onto the specimen.

cone cell Photoreceptor cell in the retina responsible for color vision.

conjugation The exchange of genetic information between two unicellular organisms.

contractile vacuoles The specialized organelle in some protists that aids in osmoregulation.

control group The group in an experiment that does not receive the independent variable.

controlled variables The parts of an experiment that are kept consistent between the control group and the experimental group.

cornea The protective transparent dome-shaped structure of the eye that aids in focusing.

corpus collosum The region of the brain that connects and communicates information between the two cerebral hemispheres.

covalent bond A strong chemical bond of shared electrons between atoms of elements.

coverslip A small transparent piece of glass or plastic that provides a flat protective surface for microscopic specimens.

crossing-over The event where some pieces of DNA are exchanged between the non-sister chromatids within the tetrad during prophase 1.

cytokinesis The process of cytoplasmic division of the cell.

cytoplasm The region between the plasma membrane and the nuclear envelope consisting of organelles and cytosol.

cytoplasmic streaming The movement of materials in the cytoplasm.

cytoskeleton The fiber-like network of proteins that maintains cell shape and allows for movement of organelles and individual cells.

cytosol Gel-like material found in the cytoplasm.

D

denaturation The breaking and alteration of a protein's molecular shape due to changes in temperature, pH, or other chemicals.

dendrites Short, highly-branched extensions that receive impulses from sensory cells or other neurons.

deoxyribonuclease The enzyme that hydrolyzes DNA polymers.

deoxyribonucleic acid (DNA) Two sequences of DNA nucleotides forming a double helix that contains genetic information.

depth of field The thickness of the layer that is in the plane of focus.

dermal papillae The uppermost layer of the dermis that attaches the upper epidermis to the capillary system.

dermis The lower layer of the skin that contains blood capillaries, glands, nerve endings, and hair follicles.

descending colon The portion of the large intestine extending down the left side toward the sigmoid colon.

diaphragm The muscle separating the thoracic and abdominal cavity that provides for inhalation and exhalation.

diastole The portion of the heartbeat when pressure on blood vessels is low during heart relaxation.

diencephalon Portion of the brain consisting of the thalamus, hypothalamus, and ventricles.

diffusion The passive movement of molecules from an area of higher concentration to an area of lower concentration.

digestion The breaking down of food materials using muscles, acids, and enzymes.

dihybrid A genetic cross producing a heterozygous offspring involving the expression of two different traits.

diploid (2n) Describes cells that contain two full sets of chromosomes.

dissecting microscope A stereomicroscope used for magnified viewing of specimens.

distal convoluted tubule (DCT) The part of a nephron positioned between the loop of Henle and the collecting duct that regulates pH and reabsorbs electrolytes.

DNA ligase The enzyme that connects the Okazaki fragments on the lagging strand during DNA replication.

DNA polymerase The enzyme that positions and joins free nucleotides according to their complementarity base in the template strand during DNA replication.

DNA replication The process that makes identical copies of DNA molecules occurring in the S phase of interphase.

dominant (genetics) An allele that masks the expression of a recessive allele.

dorsal A position of the body located toward the back side.

dorsal horn The posterior portion of the gray matter in the spinal cord that receives sensory impulses from the peripheral nervous system.

dorsal root The posterior nerve that carries sensory impulses toward the spinal cord.

dorsal root ganglion A collection of sensory neuron cell bodies in a spinal nerve carrying impulses toward the back side of the spinal cord.

duodenum The first part of the small intestine that receives chyme leaving the stomach and digestive fluids from accessory organs.

E

ear An organ that is responsible for balance and auditory processing.

ectoderm An embryonic germ layer that produces epidermis, hair, nails, skin glands, brain, spinal cord.

egg A haploid female gamete.

ejaculatory duct A tube-like structure that passes sperm and glandular fluids toward the urethra.

electrocardiogram (ECG) A test that monitors electrical activity during a heartbeat.

electron A subatomic particle with a −1 charge, found outside the nucleus of an atom.

element A specific type of atom containing a certain number of protons with unique characteristics.

elimination The release of undigested materials through the anus in animals with complete digestive systems.

Elodea **(water weed)** A genus of aquatic plant that grows entirely underwater.

embryo A developing organism.

emulsification The process where large lipid globules are fragmented into much smaller lipid globules.

endocytosis The bulk movement of molecules into a cell.

endoderm An embryonic germ layer that produces the epithelial lining of the digestive and respiratory tracts.

endometrium The interior lining of the uterus.

enzyme An organic catalyst that produces a biochemical reaction.

epidermis The outer layer of the skin; outer layer of a leaf.

epididymis A series of tubes located outside the testes that transports mature sperm to the vas deferens.

epiglottis The flap of cartilage above the larynx that closes during swallowing to prevent choking.

equilibrium When molecules move at equal rates in all directions resulting in no higher nor lower concentrations in solution.

erythrocytes Red blood cells that transport oxygen and carbon dioxide throughout the cardiovascular system.

esophagus The muscular organ of the digestive system that transports the bolus from the oral cavity to the stomach via peristalsis.

Euglena A genus of single-celled, flagellated, photosynthetic protists.

eukaryote Cells with nuclei and membrane-bound organelles.

eustachian tube The canal of the middle ear to the pharynx that equalizes pressure differences across the tympanic membrane.

exocytosis The bulk movement of molecules out of a cell.

external nares The outer opening into the nasal cavity where air is inhaled and exhaled.

eye The spherical pair of organs responsible for visual reception.

eyespot A specialized region in an organism that is sensitive to light.

F

F1 generation The first filial group of offspring produced from the cross of the parental generation.

F2 generation The second filial group of offspring produced from the cross of the F1 generation.

facilitated diffusion The passive movement of molecules from an area of higher concentration to an area of lower concentration using integral proteins (protein channels) in a plasma membrane.

fat bodies The internal masses in a frog's body cavity that stores lipids.

fertilization The fusion of gametes producing a diploid cell.

field of view The area that is seen in a microscope through the eye pieces.

filaments Thread-like series of cells.

filtrate The materials that are removed from the blood plasma during initial filtration in the kidney.

filtration The process of separating specific materials from a larger solution.

fimbriae The fingerlike projections assisting in the delivery of the egg into the oviduct.

fine focus knobs The refined adjustment on the microscope that brings the objective lenses closer or farther away from the slides.

flagellum (plural, flagella) A long hair-like structure that allows mobility of the cell.

forelimb The front leg of an animal.

fovea A concentrated collection of photoreceptors in the retina that provide for high levels of visual acuity.

frontal lobe The anterior region of the cerebrum responsible for motor movements, and higher-level thought processing.

Fungi The eukaryotic kingdom representing multicellular organisms with a chitin cell wall.

G

gallbladder The sac-shaped organ located inferior to the liver responsible for storage and release of bile for fat emulsification.

gamete Haploid sex cells (i.e., egg and sperm).

gametogenesis The production of gametes.

gas A state of matter where molecules have no fixed shape or volume.

gastrula The stage of embryo development that forms the three germ layers.

gene A sequence of DNA nucleotides that code for an RNA molecule or a protein.

gene expression The process of DNA sequences being activated to produce a sequence of RNA.

genotype The combination of alleles for a gene on two homologous chromosomes.

germ cell Specialized cell that can develop into gametes.

glial cells The cells that provide support to neurons in the nervous system.

glomerulus The capillaries found in the Bowman's capsule where blood filtration begins in the nephron.

glottis The portion in the larynx where vocal cords are located below the epiglottis.

glucose A monosaccharide of carbohydrates that has potential energy.

Golgi apparatus A series of stacked membranes in a eukaryotic cell that modifies and packages proteins to be distributed to other areas.

gonads The reproductive organs that generate gametes (i.e., ovaries and testes).

gray matter The portion of the central nervous system with nerve cells that are unmyelinated.

greater curvature The left side longer portion of the stomach that curves from the esophagus into the small intestine.

gut flora Symbiotic bacteria that reside in the colon.

H

hair cells The sensory receptors of the inner ear that contain stereocilia for hearing and balance.

hair follicle The surrounding tissue around the root of a hair.

haploid (n) Describes cells that contain only one full set of chromosomes.

heart The organ consisting of cardiac cells that rhythmically contracts and relaxes to pump blood through the circulatory system.

heart rate The number of contractions the heart takes per minute.

helicase The enzyme that unzips the DNA double helix by breaking the hydrogen bonds between complementary base pairs.

hemoglobin The protein on red blood cells that transport oxygen.

hepatocytes A functional cell of the liver.

heterozygous A genotype that has different alleles at a gene found on homologous chromosomes.

high-power lens Objective lens with 40–45x magnification.

hindlimb The back leg of an animal.

homeostasis An organism's ability to maintain a constant internal state of life-sustaining conditions.

homologous chromosomes The pairs of chromosomes in a cell that have the same genes in the same locations.

homozygous A genotype that has the same alleles at a gene found on homologous chromosomes.

hormone A molecule secreted by specialized cells that can be transported to regulate physiological processes.

hyaline cartilage A flexible supportive tissue composed of chondrocytes found at joints and the respiratory system.

hydrogen bond The weak attraction between a slight positively-charged hydrogen and another slight negatively-charged element.

hydrophilic A molecule that dissolves in water; "water-loving".

hydrophobic A molecule that does not dissolve in water; "water-fearing".

hyoid bone The U-shaped free-floating bone below the mandible located around the larynx.

hypertonic A solution that has a relatively higher concentration of solutes.

hypha Filamentous thread-like cells of fungi that make up the mycelium.

hypodermis The layer of the integument system below the skin.

hypothalamus The region of the brain below the thalamus that coordinates the pituitary gland and autonomic system.

hypothesis A proposed statement of explanation for an event that is based on observation, that can be tested, and is falsifiable.

hypotonic A solution that has a relatively lower concentration of solutes.

I

ileum The last portion of the small intestine between the jejunum and the large intestine that absorbs nutrients.

implantation The process of the embryo (blastocyst) connecting to the uterine lining (endometrium).

incomplete dominance A trait that has alleles that are not dominant nor recessive but express an intermediate phenotype in the heterozygous genotype.

independent assortment The random orientation of one pair of homologous chromosomes having no effect on the orientation of the next homologous chromosome pair during metaphase 1.

inferior vena cava The vein that brings blood from the lower body into the right atrium.

ingestion Initial acquisition of food via the mouth.

inner cell mass A collection of stem cells that give rise to the embryo.

integument The outer layers of the animal body consisting of skin (epidermis and dermis) and the hypodermis that provides protection and thermal regulation; in plants the outer covering of a seed.

intercostal muscles The muscles between the ribs that aid in moving the thoracic cavity for breathing.

internal nares The last portion of the nasal cavity before air moves into the nasopharynx.

interneurons Nerve cells that integrate incoming nerve impulses into the proper responses.

interphase The phase of the cell cycle where cell growth, organelle duplication, DNA replication, and protein synthesis occur; includes the G1, S, and G2 stages.

ion A positively- or negatively-charged particle due to the loss or gain of electrons.

ionic bond A bond that occurs between ions due to the attraction of opposite charges.

iris The colored part of the eye consisting of muscles that regulate the amount of light entering the pupil.

iris diaphragm (microscope) The adjustable microscope part under the mechanical stage that aids in regulating light intensity on the specimen.

isotonic Solutions that have an equal concentration of solutes.

J

jaws The skeletal bones (in vertebrates) forming the structure of the mouth that contain teeth.

jejunum The second part of the small intestine between the duodenum and ileum.

K

kidney The organ of the urinary system that filters blood and produces urine.

kinetochore The mobile protein structure found in the centromere of the sister chromatids that connects to microtubules in cell division.

kingdom The taxonomic level of classification below domain.

L

lagging strand The strand of DNA molecule being built away from the replication fork, discontinuously, and in fragments.

large intestine An organ of the digestive system that reabsorbs water and produces feces consisting of the cecum, colon, and rectum.

larynx The cartilaginous organ of the respiratory system that contains vocal cords used in phonation.

leading strand The strand of DNA molecule being built continuously in the 5' to 3' direction going towards the replication fork.

left atrium The left upper chamber of the heart that receives blood from the pulmonary system.

left ventricle The left lower chamber of the heart that receives blood from the left atrium.

lens A thin layer of transparent cells behind the iris and opening of the pupil.

lesser curvature The right, shorter portion, of the stomach that curves from the esophagus into the small intestine.

leukocytes Specialized blood cells involved with the immune response known as white blood cells.

Lithobates catesbeianus Species name of the bullfrog.

liver An accessory organ of the digestive system composed of hepatocytes that detoxifies blood, processes carbohydrates, vitamins, and lipids, and produces bile.

loop of Henle The U-shaped portion of the nephron tubule that descends into the renal medulla and ascends back to the renal cortex that reabsorbs water and sodium chloride.

low-power lens Objective lens with 10x magnification.

lumen The inner area of a tube-like structure.

lung The organ of the respiratory system containing alveoli that function in gas exchange.

lysosome An animal organelle that contains hydrolytic enzymes to break apart molecules and worn out organelles.

M

macromolecule A large molecule formed by the bonding between smaller molecules.

mass number The collective number of protons and neutrons in an atom.

matter Anything with mass and volume.

maxillary teeth The teeth located on the outer margin of the upper jaw.

mechanical digestion The physical breaking of food items into smaller pieces through muscular action.

mechanical stage The location of the microscope where slides are placed for viewing specimens.

mechanoreceptors A specialized cell that detects sound and touch.

medulla oblongata The portion of the brain stem continuous with the superior end of the spinal cord.

meiosis Specialized cell division that produces haploid cells.

mesoderm An embryonic germ layer that produces heart, blood vessels, wall of digestive and respiratory tracts, muscle, bone.

messenger RNA (mRNA) A sequence of RNA nucleotides produced during transcription that can code for a protein sequence during translation.

metaphase Stage of mitosis when sister chromatids align along the equator of the cell.

microtubules Protein filaments that assist in providing structure to the cell and moving organelles; forms the mitotic spindle to assist moving chromosomes during cell division.

microvilli Plasma projections of the epithelial layer in the small intestine that increases surface area for absorption.

micturition The process of urination.

midbrain Connects the pons to the diencephalon and serves as another relay center for sensory input and motor output.

mitochondria The double membrane bound organelle that performs aerobic respiration producing ATP energy for eukaryotic cells.

mitosis Nuclear division that produces identical daughter cells.

mitotic spindle Thread-like structures composed of microtubules that aid in dividing chromosomes during cell division.

molecule Structure produced when two or more atoms held together by chemical bonds.

monohybrid A genetic cross producing a heterozygous offspring involving the expression of a single trait.

monosaccharide A monomer of carbohydrates.

morula A small solid cluster of embryonic cells.

motor neurons Deliver nerve impulses away from the CNS to the muscles and glands.

mucosa A membranous lining of various body cavities or internal organs.

multicellular An organism consisting of many interdependent cells.

multipolar neurons Nerve cells with multiple dendritic branches and a single axon extending directly from the cell body.

muscularis A layer of smooth muscle found in the walls of contracting organs.

myelin sheath A protective fatty tissue consisting of Schwann cells that surrounds axons to speed nervous impulses.

N

nasal cavity The chamber of the respiratory system receiving air from the external nares which warms, moistens, and filters the incoming air; contains chemoreceptors for detecting molecules for the sense of smell.

near point The closest distance at which the eye can focus on an object.

negative-pressure breathing The process of the diaphragm contraction that increases the volume of the thoracic cavity that decreases the forces in the lungs resulting in air being sucked into the lungs.

nephron The functional unit of the kidney that produces urine.

nerve Structures composed of myelinated axons of sensory and motor neurons bundled together with glial cells in layers of connective tissue.

neural tube Embryo structure produced during neurulation that will become the future brain and spinal cord.

neurons Highly-branched, elongated nerve cells that carry chemical electrical impulses

neurula The stage of embryo development that generates the neural tube.

neutron A subatomic particle with a mass of 1amu, and no charge, found inside the nucleus of an atom.

nictitating membrane A semi-transparent membrane of the amphibian eye that rises to keep the eye moist, clean, and protected during diving.

nitrogenous base A nitrogen-rich molecule that is part of the nucleotide structure (i.e., adenine, cytosine, guanine, thymine, or uracil).

Nodes of Ranvier The small gaps of exposed axon found along the nerve cell.

nonpolar A molecule, or a region of a molecule, that shares electrons equally between atoms and has no partial charge.

notochord The supporting flexible rod important in vertebra development that is derived from the mesoderm.

nuclear envelope The double phospholipid bilayers that surround and protect the DNA in eukaryotes.

nucleic acid An organic macromolecule composed of nucleotides that carry genetic information and aid in expressing proteins.

nucleoid Region in a prokaryotic cell consisting of the circular chromosome made of DNA.

nucleolus A region within the nucleus of eukaryotes where ribosomes are synthesized.

nucleotide The monomer of nucleic acids consisting of three chemical components: a **phosphate** group, a 5-carbon **sugar**, and a nitrogen-containing **base**.

nucleus The core of an atom consisting of protons and neutrons, except in hydrogen (chemistry); the organelle that houses the DNA, chromosomes, in a cell (biology).

O

objective lens The parts of a microscope connected to the rotating nosepiece that provides magnification in viewing specimens.

occipital lobe The posterior region of the cerebrum responsible for visual processing.

octet rule The statement that an atom is stable when it has 8 electrons in its outer shell; exceptions occur when atoms only utilize the first shell that is stable having 2 electrons.

ocular lens The part of a microscope in the eyepiece that magnifies specimens.

oil immersion lens Objective lens with 100x magnification that requires an oil bridge.

Okazaki fragments The small sections of DNA replicated discontinuously on the lagging strand.

oogenesis The production of egg (ova) cells.

optic nerve The collection of neurons transmitting impulses between the eye and brain.

oral cavity The location of the mouth behind the teeth and gums where food enters the digestive system and begins mechanical and chemical digestion.

organ A collection of tissues working together for a common function.

organ system A collection of related organs working together for a common function.

organelle A collection of molecules that make up the structure of cells and carry out cellular functions.

organism An individual living entity consisting of one or multiple cells.

organogenesis The development of organs.

osmosis The facilitated diffusion of *water* across a semipermeable membrane.

ossicle Any of the 3 small bones in the middle ear responsible for receiving and amplifying vibrations to the oval window.

ovary The female gonad where eggs (oocytes) are produced and that generates the sex hormones estrogen and progesterone.

oviduct The fallopian tube that transports the ova to the uterus.

oviducts The tube-like structures that receive the egg (oocyte) from the ovary and transports it to the uterus; site of fertilization.

ovulation The rupturing of the follicle and the release of the secondary oocyte from an ovary.

ovum (plural, ova) A haploid female gamete.

oxygen, O_2 The molecule that hemoglobin carries to cells for aerobic respiration.

P

P generation The parents in a genetic cross between organisms.

P wave The first wave in an ECG when the atria depolarize during the contraction.

pancreas An accessory organ of the digestive system that produces digestive enzymes; a gland of the endocrine system that produces hormones.

pancreatic amylase An enzyme produced by the pancreas that hydrolyzes starch and glycogen into monosaccharides.

pancreatic lipase An enzyme produced by the pancreas that hydrolyzes lipids into glycerol and fatty acids.

Paramecium A genus of single-celled freshwater protists that belong to a group broadly known as the ciliates.

parfocal capability The capability of microscopes to keep the image in focus when changing magnification.

parietal lobe The superior region of the cerebrum responsible for somatosensory processing.

passive transport The transport of molecules that does not require the use of energy.

pellicle A series of flexible protein strips that wrap around the cell membrane in *Euglena*.

penis The male urogenital organ that transfers semen during copulation; also functions in the elimination of urine.

pepsin The active enzyme in the stomach that hydrolyzes proteins.

peripheral nervous system (PNS) The portion of the nervous system consisting of the cranial nerves and spinal nerves that extend throughout the body relaying information to and from the central nervous system.

peristalsis The involuntary wavelike muscular contractions of the digestive system that move materials forward through the lumen.

peritoneum The connective tissue lining the body cavity.

peritubular capillaries The capillaries that surround the tubules of a nephron allowing for the exchange of materials.

peroxisomes A spherical organelle that oxidizes fatty acids and contains catalase.

pH scale The measurement of the concentration of hydrogen ions in a substance ranging from 0–14.

phalange The digital bones located in fingers and toes at the distal region of a limb.

pharynx The location behind the nose and mouth where the respiratory and digestive pathways transport air and food respectively.

phenotype The physical expression of a gene.

phospholipid A type of lipid with two non-polar fatty acids and a polar phosphate group attached to a glycerol molecule found making up membranes.

photoreceptors Specialized cells in sensory organs that are sensitive and respond to light.

phototaxis The detection of light and subsequent movement towards the light source.

pili Short hair-like structures on the surface of some bacteria; sometimes called fimbria.

pinna The external structure extending from the auditory canal of the ear; the auricle.

pituitary gland The master control gland of the endocrine system located at the base of the brain consisting of an anterior and posterior region.

plane of focus The specific layer in focus throughout a depth of field viewable in a microscope.

Plantae The eukaryotic kingdom representing multicellular photosynthetic organisms with a cellulose cell wall.

plasma The non-cellular fluid of the blood that consists of dissolved materials.

plasma membrane A phospholipid bilayer containing proteins that acts as a semipermeable barrier between the cell and the outer environment.

plasmolysis The shrinking of plant cells within their cell walls resulting from a loss of water from their vacuoles.

polar A molecule, or a region of a molecule, that has electrons that are pulled unequally between atoms that results in partial positive and negative charges.

polar body A small cell divided from the oocytes during meiosis 1 and 2.

polygenic inheritance A pattern of inheritance where a single trait is controlled by more than one gene.

polypeptide A polymer of proteins composed of long chains of amino acids bonded together.

polysaccharide A polymer of carbohydrates composed of long chains of monosaccharides bonded together.

pons The bulging portion of the brain stem superior to the medulla.

posterior A position of the body located toward the rear.

presbyopia Age-related loss of lens elasticity.

primary follicles An immature cavity that surrounds the developing oocyte in the ovary.

primary oocytes A female germ cell that starts dividing during meiosis 1 that produces a secondary oocyte and a polar body.

primary spermatocyte A male germ cell that starts dividing during meiosis 1 that produces two secondary spermatocytes.

primer A small section of RNA built to allow DNA polymerase to initiate replication of the DNA.

primitive gut The cavity produced during gastrulation consisting of endoderm that begins the formation of the digestive system; the archenteron.

prokaryote Unicellular organisms that lack a nuclear membrane to surround their DNA.

prophase Stage of mitosis when sister chromatids condense, and the nucleus begins to break down.

prostate gland An organ at the base of the urinary bladder, surrounding the urethra of males, that secretes an alkaline fluid into the semen during ejaculation.

protein An organic macromolecule composed of one or more strands of amino acids.

Protista The eukaryotic kingdom representing an artificial classification consisting of varied organisms.

proton A subatomic particle with a mass of 1amu, and a +1 charge, found inside the nucleus of an atom.

proximal convoluted tubule (PCT) The part of a nephron positioned between the Bowman's capsule and loop of Henle that aids in pH regulation and reabsorbs Na$^+$, glucose, and amino acids.

pulmonary artery Blood vessel carrying oxygen poor blood away from the right ventricle to the lung.

pulmonary circuit The blood leaving the right side of the heart, crossing the lungs, and returning via the pulmonary veins.

pulmonary semi-lunar valve The valve of the heart preventing a backflow of blood from the pulmonary artery to the right ventricle.

pulmonary vein Blood vessel carrying oxygenated blood into the left atrium.

Punnett square A tool used to predict the genotype of offspring of a genetic cross.

pupil The opening of the iris that allows light to be received by the lens of the eye.

Purkinje fibers Branches of nerves that send impulses into the ventricles of the heart causing the cardiac contraction.

pyloric sphincter Area of smooth muscle that regulates the movement of chyme from the stomach into the duodenum.

Q

QRS wave The largest wave in an ECG when the ventricles depolarize during the contraction.

R

reabsorption The process of moving materials back into a previously located area.

recessive An allele that is masked by a dominant allele; only expressed when found on both homologous chromosomes (homozygous).

recombination The incorporation or replacement of sections of DNA from other sources (viruses, bacteria), causing increased genetic variation. Genetic engineering creates recombinant DNA by the splicing of nucleotide sequences into existing DNA molecules.

rectum The area of the large intestine that collects and stores feces before elimination.

reflex Involuntary responses involving nerve impulses.

reflex arc The path travelled by the involuntary nerve impulses.

renal artery The blood vessel carrying blood into the kidney.

renal corpuscle The collective Bowman's capsule and glomerulus.

renal cortex The outer layer of the kidney that contains the renal corpuscles and much of the renal tubules.

renal medulla The darker layer of the kidney just below the cortex appearing as repeating renal pyramids that consist of nephron loops and collecting ducts.

renal pelvis A smooth inner layer of the kidney that fills with urine from the collecting ducts.

renal vein The blood vessel carrying blood from the kidney.

replication fork The Y-shaped location on a replicating DNA strand that is unzipping due to helicase.

resolving power (microscope) The ability of a microscope to distinguish between two adjacent points.

retina The layer of photoreceptive cells (cones and rods) in the back of the eye where light waves stimulate impulses to be sent through the optic nerve.

retroperitoneal The location behind the peritoneum.

revolving nosepiece (microscope) The part of a microscope that rotates to allow selection of objective lenses.

rhizoids Small filamentous threads of cells that anchor and conduct materials in some plants and fungi.

Rhizopus A genus of a common bread mold.

ribonuclease An enzyme that hydrolyzes RNA polymers into smaller molecules.

ribonucleic acid (RNA) A single stranded nucleic acid that assists in expressing genes.

ribosomal RNA (rRNA) A sequence of RNA nucleotides making the structural composition of the ribosome.

ribosome Organelle where protein synthesis occurs consisting of protein and RNA nucleotides.

right atrium The right upper chamber of the heart that receives blood from the systemic system.

right ventricle The right lower chamber of the heart that receives blood from the right atrium.

RNA polymerase The enzyme that travels along the gene breaking the hydrogen bonds between complementary bases and building RNA by base-pairing with one of the DNA strands.

rod cell Photoreceptor cells in the retina that are sensitive to low light intensity.

rough endoplasmic reticulum (rough ER) Interconnected membranes in a eukaryotic cell that hold ribosomes and can modify proteins.

rugae The folds of the stomach that allow for expansion.

S

saccule The smaller sac in the inner ear containing hair cells and otoliths.

saliva An aqueous mixture of digestive enzymes and mucus produced by salivary glands that's released into the oral cavity.

salivary amylase An enzyme produced by the salivary glands that hydrolyzes starch and glycogen into monosaccharides.

salivary glands The three pairs of exocrine organs that secrete saliva into the oral cavity providing lubrication and aid in chemical digestion.

salts Compounds composed of acids that have metals or other cations replacing the hydrogen.

saprotroph An organism that feeds off decaying organic material (e.g. ,mold, bacteria).

scanning electron microscope (SEM) A device that uses negatively charged particles (electrons) to bombard a specimen to produce a highly detailed image.

scanning lens Objective lens with 4x magnification.

Schwann cells The cells of the myelin sheath that wrap around axons.

science A logical, investigative process to obtain knowledge in the study of the physical and natural world.

scientific method The process of research that includes observation, questioning, hypothesis development, predictions, experimentation, and careful analysis of results.

sclera The protective outer layer (white) of the eye.

scrotum The external sac-like structure in males that contain the testis and epididymis outside the body cavity.

sebaceous gland A gland in the dermis that secretes sebum (oil) to moisturize the hair and epidermis.

secondary follicle A maturing cavity that surrounds the developing oocyte in the ovary containing the theca layers that produce hormones and support the follicle.

secondary oocyte A haploid female germ cell that divides during meiosis 2 that, after this division, produces a mature haploid ovum.

secondary spermatocyte A haploid male germ cell that divides during meiosis 2 that, after this division, produces two haploid spermatids.

secretion A process of discharging materials from a structure.

semen A mixture of sperm and glandular secretions.

semicircular canals The three tube-like structures in the inner ear that are positioned in all represented planes of the body that aid in maintaining balance.

semiconservative replication Describes DNA replication where one original strand is read and only one new complimentary strand is produced; this occurs to both original strands of the double helix resulting in the two new DNA molecules consisting of one old and one new strand.

seminal vesicles The glands of the reproductive system that adds ejaculatory fluids (mainly fructose) to the junction of the vas deferens and urethra.

seminiferous tubules The series of coiled tubules within separate lobules of each testis.

semipermeable A membranous structure that allows some substances, but not all, to pass through.

sensory neurons Transmit nerve impulses to the CNS.

sensory receptors Specialized nerve cells that detect changes in the environment.

sigmoid The S-shaped portion of the large intestine between the descending colon and rectum.

simple diffusion The net directional movement of the solute from areas of higher solute concentration towards areas of lower solute concentration.

sinoatrial (SA) node The major part of the cardiac conduction system that generates impulses to the AV node and conducted through the heart.

sister chromatid The identical portion of a replicated chromosome held together at the centromere.

skeletal muscle Cells consisting of myosin and actin that are attached to bones; contract to produce movements.

skin The outer protective layer covering an organism.

small intestine The portion of the digestive system between the stomach and large intestine (consisting of the duodenum, jejunum, and ileum) where chemical digestion and absorption occurs.

smooth endoplasmic reticulum (smooth ER) Interconnected membranes in a eukaryotic cell that can produce lipids, process carbohydrates, and detoxifies the cell.

smooth muscle Involuntary contractile cells found in internal organs that produces bodily movements (e.g., peristalsis in the digestive system).

soft palate The fleshy part of the oral cavity behind the hard palate.

solutes A substance that is dissolved by solvents.

solution A mixture of dissolved solutes in a solvent.

solvent A substance that dissolves solutes.

somatic cells The non-germ cells of a multicellular organism.

somites The blocks of mesodermal tissue around the neural tube that will give rise to the vertebrae and ribs.

sperm A haploid male gamete.

spermatids Immature sperm cells.

spermatogenesis The production of sperm cells.

spermatogonium The diploid male germ cells in seminiferous tubules that produce primary spermatocytes through the process of mitosis.

spinal cord The portion of the central nervous system that connects the spinal nerves of the body to the brain.

spirillum Corkscrew-shaped bacteria.

Spirogyra A genus of freshwater algae consisting of cylindrical cells that attach to one another in long filaments and is photosynthetic.

sporangiophore A structure that contains spore-producing sporangia.

sporangium A container where spores are produced.

spore A haploid single-cell in plants and some other eukaryotes.

stage (microscope) The part of a microscope where slides are placed to view specimens.

stage adjustment knobs (microscope) The part of a microscope that moves a slide around the field of view.

starch A highly branched polysaccharide that stores energy in plants.

start codon The codon on mRNA (AUG) that initiates the process of translation.

steroid A type of lipid composed of interlocking carbon rings.

stolon An aboveground stem that roots to form new plant positions.

stomach The organ of the digestive system between the esophagus and small intestine that aids in protein digestion.

stop codon One of three codons on mRNA (UAG, UAA, or UGA) that terminates the process of translation.

submucosa A layer of tissue in the gastrointestinal tract that supports and joins the mucosa to the lower smooth muscle.

substrate A reactant of an enzymatic chemical reaction.

superior vena cava The vein that brings blood from the upper body into the right atrium.

sweat gland A gland in the dermis of the skin that produces liquids to reduce body temperature.

synapses The small gap between axon terminals and other neurons; site of neurotransmitter release.

synapsis The process of homologous chromosomes organizing and connecting during prophase 1.

systemic circuit The blood leaving the left side of the heart and passing throughout the body except the lungs before returning to the heart in the vena cavae.

systole The portion of the heartbeat when contraction occurs putting pressure on blood vessels.

T

T wave The third wave in an ECG when the ventricles repolarize.

teeth The hard enamel structures connected to the jaws used by most vertebrates to masticate food.

telophase Stage of mitosis when chromosomes loosen into chromatin and the new nuclear envelope forms.

temperature The measurement of molecular motion.

template strand The strand of DNA that is copied into mRNA during transcription.

temporal lobe The lateral region of the cerebrum responsible for auditory processing.

testis The male gonad that produces sperm and testosterone.

tetrad A pair of homologous chromosomes in synapsis during prophase 1.

thalamus A portion of the diencephalon that acts as the relay center to send impulses to and from the cerebral cortex.

theory A highly supported and confirmed statement in science that explains the events of the natural and physical world.

thrombocytes Cellular fragments, known as platelets, that help clot blood to stop bleeding.

thyroid cartilage The connective tissue supporting the larynx (Adam's apple) in the respiratory system.

tissue A collection of related cells working together for a common function.

tongue The muscular organ of the oral cavity, used in speech and taste reception, that manipulates the bolus and initiates swallowing.

tonicity The relative concentration of solutes in one solution as compared to another solution.

trachea The cartilaginous organ of the respiratory system that provides flexibility and support to transport air to the bronchi.

trait A characteristic of an organism based on the specific DNA sequences of one or more genes.

transcription The process of producing a strand of messenger RNA (mRNA) from a gene in DNA.

transfer RNA (tRNA) The molecule that carries an amino acid to the ribosome, specific to the anti-codon, to add to the growing polypeptide sequence.

translation The process of joining amino acids together to build a protein at the site of the ribosome.

transport vesicles Small membranous organelles that carry materials to specific regions in a cell.

transverse colon The portion of the large intestine between the ascending and descending colon.

tricuspid valve The valve of the heart preventing a backflow of blood from the right ventricle to the right atrium.

triglyceride A fat or oil molecule consisting of three fatty acids attached to a glycerol molecule.

truncus arteriosus Artery leaving the ventricle in the amphibian heart.

trypsin An enzyme that hydrolyzes proteins in the small intestine.

tympanic membrane A thin layer of tissue that receives sound waves from the outer ear and passes vibrational waves to the middle ear.

U

unicellular An organism consisting of a single independent cell.

urea A nitrogenous, organic waste product of protein metabolism that is found in urine.

ureters The tube-like structures that transport urine from the kidneys to the urinary bladder.

urethra The tube-like structure that releases urine from the urinary bladder to be expelled from the body; in males it also releases semen during ejaculation.

urinary bladder The muscular sac-like organ of the urinary system that stores urine before elimination through the urethra.

urine A solution of urea, salts, and water that is produced and excreted by the urinary system.

uterus The organ of the female reproductive system that is where gestation of the developing embryo occurs.

utricle A small sac in the inner ear containing hair cells and otoliths that send signals to the brain concerning the position of the head.

V

vacuole A membrane-bound organelle that stores and can transport water and other cellular material.

vagina The orifice of the female reproductive system that receives the penis during copulation and semen upon ejaculation; acts as the birth canal.

vas deferens The tubular structure in the male reproductive system that transports sperm from the epididymis to the ejaculatory duct.

veins Blood vessels that return low-pressure blood back into the heart.

vena cava The blood vessel (vein) carrying blood from the systemic system into the right atrium.

ventral A position of the body located toward the abdominal side.

ventral horn The anterior portion of the gray matter in the spinal cord that initiates motor impulses toward the peripheral nervous system.

ventral root The anterior nerve that carries motor impulses away from the spinal cord.

vesicle A small membrane-bound organelle that transports materials in the cell; can also fuse with membranes to move materials through bulk transport.

vestibule The part of the inner ear that is responsible for responding to rotational movements and changes of the head in respect to gravity.

villi Fingerlike projections of the small intestine that increases surface area for absorption.

viruses A non-living protein capsule containing nucleic acids that is of organic composition requiring a host cell.

vitamins A type of organic molecule that aids in maintaining regular cellular activities.

vocal folds The membranous tissues in the larynx that vibrate when air is forced outward (exhalation) to produce sounds.

voluntary reactions Responses to stimuli that are initiated consciously.

vomerine teeth The top projections in a frog's oral cavity that can secure prey items for ingestion.

W

white matter The portion of the central nervous system with nerve cells surrounded by myelin sheaths.

X

X-linked A gene located on the X chromosome.

Y

yolk The nutrient-rich region of protein and lipids in a developing embryo.

Z

zona pellucida An encapsulating membrane surrounding a secondary oocyte.

zygote The diploid cell produced from the fertilization of an egg cell (n) by a sperm cell (n).